EDThoughts

What We Know About Mathematics Teaching and Learning

edited by
John Sutton and Alice Krueger
Mid-continent Research for Education and Learning

Mid-continent Research for Education and Learning

A collaborative publication from

and

ASSM

Association of State Supervisors of Mathematics

**Association of State Supervisors
of Mathematics**

**The National Network of
Eisenhower Regional Consortia
and Clearinghouse**

Published by

**Mid-continent Research for
Education and Learning**
2550 S. Parker Road, Suite 500
Aurora, CO 80014-1678
(303) 337-0990
www.mcrel.org

Fractal image on front cover courtesy of Paul W. Carlson.
The program that created the fractal image on the front cover is
available on a CD along with 730 fractal images. A school site license
costs $30. No previous knowledge of fractals or mathematics is
required. For Windows 95/98/ME/2000/NT4/Xp. For more
information, visit http://www.mbfractals.com

ISBN No. 1-893476-02-2

This book was produced in whole or in part with funds from the U.S. Department of Education National
Eisenhower Mathematics and Science Programs Office of Educational Research and Improvement (OERI),
under grant R168R950025-00. The content does not necessarily reflect the position or policy of OERI or the
Department of Education or any other agency of the federal government.

Acknowledgements

Contributing Authors
Gary Appel, NCREL
Malcolm Butler, SERVE
Anne Collins, Massachusetts, ASSM
Ella-Mae Daniel, SERVE
Elaine DeBassige D'Amato, McREL
Judy Florian, McREL
Fred Gross, TERC
Jodean Grunow, Wisconsin, ASSM
Carol Hanley, Kentucky, CSSS
Clare Heidema, McREL
Bill Hopkins, Texas, ASSM
Deb Jordan, McREL
Mozell Lang, Michigan, CSSS
Arlene Mitchell, McREL
Brett Moulding, Utah, CSSS
Randi Peterson, McREL
Gwen Pollock, Illinois, CSSS
Linda Schoen, South Carolina, CSSS
Sharon Stenglein, Minnesota, ASSM
Jan Tuomi, McREL
Jim Woodland, Nebraska, CSSS

Editors
Jim Harper, RBS
Barbara Hicks, AEL
Nancy Kellogg
Carolyn Richbart
Lynn Richbart
Vicki Urquhart, McREL
Janie Zimmer, RBS

Librarians
Linda Brannan, McREL
Norma Brown, McREL
Terry Young, McREL

Graphics and Layout
Dawn McGill, McREL
Molly Drew, McREL

Indexing
James Sucha, McREL

Dear *EdThoughts* Reader,

Many good intentions have gone into ambitious education reform goals, including those ratified by the U.S. Congress in 1985. But the year 2000 deadline has passed, and our nation has not made measurable progress toward the goal of becoming "first in the world in mathematics and science education."

In international comparisons, our students' overall mathematics and science achievement is mediocre. The Third International Mathematics and Science Study (TIMSS) from 1995 showed our 3rd- and 4th-graders scoring above the international average but our 12th-graders scoring well below. The TIMSS-Repeat results released in 2000 do not show significant improvement. What can we do to make a difference?

EDThoughts provides a place to start. The mathematics and science *EDThoughts* books summarize educational research and surveys of best classroom practices, and they offer implications for improved teaching and learning.

Classroom teachers and K–12 administrators will find these books useful for their own professional development; teacher educators can use them to inspire their students, and parents and the public can read about the intended and achieved results of educational practices. Effective reforms in mathematics and science education practice and policy will require the collaboration of all of these stakeholder groups. They will need a common understanding of the current status of mathematics and science education and of the direction that research and best practice indicate for improvement as well as how they can help accomplish reform. We hope that this book provides a foundation for greater understanding and reflection.

Please take a moment to fill out and return the postcard enclosed in this volume. You then will be sent a short survey that will help us to design useful supporting materials and products and to keep this document fresh. Your participation is sincerely appreciated.

John Sutton
McREL

Alice Krueger
McREL

Kim Gattis
ASSM

Table of Contents

Dear *EDThoughts* Reader i

Questions Addressed in Each Section iv

Preface vii

About the *EDThoughts* Books ix

Mathematics For All...1

Teaching Mathematics..11

Assessment in Mathematics...33

Mathematics Curriculum 43

Instructional Technology in Mathematics 61

Learning Mathematics 73

References 101

Index...111

Questions Addressed in Each Section

Mathematics For All

- What is equity and how is it evident in mathematics classrooms?
- What are the impacts of ability grouping and tracking on student learning?
- What can schools do to facilitate students' opportunity to learn mathematics?
- How can different learning styles be addressed with consistent expectations?

Teaching Mathematics

- What instructional methods support mathematical reasoning and problem solving?
- How is mathematical thinking addressed in the mathematics classroom?
- What role does teacher questioning play in learning mathematics?
- How can teachers motivate students to enjoy and want to learn mathematics?
- What instructional strategies make mathematics teaching more learner-centered?
- How does linking instruction and classroom assessment impact student learning?
- How does teacher content knowledge impact instruction?
- How does teacher pedagogical knowledge impact instruction?
- How do teacher attitudes about mathematics learning impact student achievement?
- What are the characteristics of effective professional development for mathematics?

Assessment in Mathematics

- What roles can assessment play in mathematics teaching and learning?
- How can the use of varied assessments provide important evidence of learning?
- How can mathematical thinking be assessed in the classroom?
- What do national/international assessments tell us about teaching and learning mathematics?

Mathematics Curriculum

- What is the importance of standards-based curricula in mathematics?
- How do we determine what students should know and be able to do in mathematics?
- What is curriculum coherence and articulation?

- What is the importance of reading and writing in the mathematics curriculum?
- What are the most important considerations in selecting textbooks and other materials?
- In what ways can integrating curriculum enhance learning in mathematics?
- How does integrated instruction in mathematics affect teaching and learning?
- How does classroom curriculum connect to the outside world?

Instructional Technology in Mathematics
- How can using instructional technology affect mathematics reasoning and problem solving?
- What effect do calculators have on student learning?
- How can technology make mathematics teaching more learner-centered?
- How can students best use information and data from the Internet?
- How has technology changed the mathematics that is important for students to learn?

Learning Mathematics
- How can we communicate with the public about the importance of learning mathematics?
- What do we know about how students learn mathematics?
- What does learning theory show teachers about how students learn mathematics?
- What is the role of basic skills in mathematics instruction?
- What is the role of algorithms in mathematics instruction?
- What factors contribute most strongly to students' success in learning mathematics?
- How do students' attitudes affect their performance and future opportunities?
- How can teachers help students reflect on and communicate their own learning?
- What role does active hands-on learning play in mathematics instruction?
- How does using contextual or applied activities improve student learning in mathematics?
- What can parents do to support student learning in mathematics?
- What are characteristics of effective homework in mathematics?
- What is the impact of teacher learning on student learning?

Preface

The world around us is changing rapidly. There have been changes in how people live, work, and learn. Likewise, the culture and practice of mathematics continue to evolve. These changes signal the need for reform in mathematics education. As students increasingly are educated to become lifelong learners, they must develop skills to manage and use knowledge to solve problems in the personal, social, and economic realms, not just in textbooks. Today's students will need to build their capabilities for career changes, more so than at any time in the past. Most twenty-first century careers are knowledge-based, not skill-based. Knowing how to access, evaluate, and use information is a major component of mathematics literacy.

New knowledge, tools, and ways of doing or communicating mathematics continue to emerge and evolve. Students today need mathematics skills, concepts, and understandings different from those needed by their parents and grandparents. The level of mathematics needed for intelligent citizenship has increased dramatically, along with increased needs for mathematical thinking and problem solving.

Mathematics is critical to the education of all students, not just for a select few. *Principles and Standards for School Mathematics* (also known as the National Council of Teachers of Mathematics or NCTM *Standards*, and abbreviated *PSSM*) describes a vision of a mathematically powerful student and offers a set of goals for mathematics instruction — the basic skills and understandings students will need to function effectively in the twenty-first century. Enhanced career opportunities do and will exist for those who understand and can do mathematics. Mathematics education should prepare students who can use mathematics appropriately in their careers and their lives.

The purpose of this volume is to support standards-based reform of mathematics education. For each question addressed, background is provided from the perspectives of research and best practices, followed by implications for improving classroom instruction.

Teachers need the findings from research and best practices to inform their daily decisions. It is ineffective for teachers to base decisions on anecdotal information or individual cases. Part of the decision-making process requires teacher expertise (knowledge and experience) in determining whether the practices being considered for adoption will work in their own classrooms. Using data to drive instructional decisions improves the efficiency of reform efforts by focusing change in the desired direction — toward improved student achievement.

The authors of this volume strongly support standards-based systemic reform. They recognize that the national mathematics standards describe not only important curricular content, but also ways to reform all parts of the educational system to support improved teaching and student achievement. Systemic reform purposefully revises and aligns all components of a system. The mathematics education system is complex, including components such as assessment, curriculum, equity, student outcome standards, teaching, professional development of teachers, stakeholder involvement, leadership, and policy. While the last three topics are generally beyond the scope of this volume, they are important in the context of standards-based systemic reform.

Every person concerned with teaching and learning mathematics, whether teacher, administrator, student, parent, or community member, will find useful information in this document. As the nation moves forward in reform of mathematics education, we must apply lessons learned from research and best practices. These will guide us toward the improvement of our students' achievement — a goal we cannot afford to ignore.

About the *EDThoughts* Books

This series of books is intended to bring to K–12 educators the rich world of educational research and best practices. As classroom teachers are mainly concerned with what works in their own classrooms, these documents balance reporting research results with drawing implications from it. Thus each pertinent question is addressed through both a page of Research and Best Practice and a page of Classroom Implications.

The background research and related documents for each question are cited in compressed format in the margin bar on the right page. There is a full citation of all References in the back of the book to allow the reader to examine the primary source documents. It is the intent of the authors that the format of the *EDThoughts* books will encourage classroom teachers to delve into the available results of educational research and apply the findings to improve the achievement of all their students.

The list of authors for the *EDThoughts* mathematics and science books includes state content consultants belonging to both the Association of State Supervisors of Mathematics (ASSM) and the Council of State Supervisors of Science (CSSS), and mathematics and science experts from several Eisenhower Regional Consortia. The editors belong to Eisenhower Regional Consortia, Regional Educational Laboratories, and other national organizations. With such wide geographic representation among authors and editors, the reader may expect to find an equally wide range of perspectives represented.

There are unifying threads throughout all the articles. One common element is the authors' reliance on the national standards, the National Council of Teachers of Mathematics *Principles and Standards for School Mathematics*, as a compilation of best practices. It would have been possible to list this document as a Reference for every question. Another common theme is the importance of quality mathematics education for all students. The reader will also notice the frequency with which professional development needs are stated in the Classroom Implications sections. The presence of these common themes shows the consistency of approach of the diverse authors.

Mathematics For All

All students can learn mathematics, and they deserve the opportunity to do so. The National Council of Teachers of Mathematics (NCTM) *Principles and Standards for School Mathematics* (*PSSM*) sets forth mathematics literacy expectations for all students and describes what all students are expected to learn. However, recognizing the diversity among our nation's children, educators do not expect all students to learn the material in the same manner, using the same resources, and in the same time frame. The Equity Principle in *PSSM* states:

> *All students, regardless of their personal characteristics, backgrounds, or physical challenges, must have opportunities to study – and support to learn – mathematics. Equity does not mean that every student should receive identical instruction; instead, it demands that reasonable and appropriate accommodations be made as needed to promote access and attainment for all students. (p.12)*

To achieve "mathematics for all" will take a concerted effort from all stakeholders in our children's education. We must continue to make progress toward providing rich, well-supported learning environments that respond to the unique educational needs of every student. That is the goal of mathematics education reform.

What is equity and how is it evident in mathematics classrooms?

An equitable mathematics program provides high-quality mathematics education for all students.

Research and Best Practice

An equitable mathematics program provides high-quality mathematics education for all students. Students not only have access to quality mathematics courses and instruction, but they also have the support necessary to ensure their success in those courses. Equitable school programs must assure that student differences in achievement will not be based on race/ethnicity, gender, or physical disability, and that appropriate instructional support will be provided for each student to ensure success for all.

A successful educational system focuses on student outcomes and provides the support necessary for every student to achieve them. Differences in mathematics achievement among various gender, income, and ethnic groups have been widely reported. However, the National Research Council did not find significant gender differences among male and female students who had taken the same mathematics coursework. Lower-socioeconomic status (SES) students and those belonging to minority groups who took high school algebra and geometry attended college in percentages approximately equal to higher-SES white students who had enrolled in the same high school courses. Research findings also indicated that younger and lower-ability students could learn and employ the same strategies and skills for mathematical reasoning and thinking as those used by older and higher-ability students.

Since achievement in higher-level mathematics serves as a gatekeeper to success in higher education and in 21st century careers, it is important to note that group achievement differences in mathematics are often attributable to enrollment patterns or instructional strategies. Low-SES students and those of color are half as likely to enroll in higher-level mathematics courses as higher-SES white students. Girls typically learn better through cooperative rather than traditional competitive instructional strategies. Since different students learn in different ways, equal treatment for all students does not guarantee equal success. Mathematics teachers and school counselors need to facilitate equal access to algebra, geometry, and higher-level mathematics courses and see that the support required to be successful in these programs is provided for all students.

Classroom Implications

To create an equitable classroom, teachers use a variety of strategies to reach all students with high-quality content. These strategies include

- Clearly identifying the knowledge students need to master
- Addressing different student learning styles
- Encouraging the participation of under-represented students
- Challenging all students
- Diagnosing where students are struggling to learn and providing appropriate instruction
- Embedding a variety of assessment types throughout units of study
- Engaging all students in higher-order thinking skills (e.g., data analysis, synthesis of results, and evaluation of potential solutions)
- Helping students make connections among related mathematics concepts, across other disciplines (e.g., science and social studies) and related to everyday experiences
- Encouraging participation by all students
- Fostering the use of inclusionary language in all classroom communication
- Involving parents in student learning

Adequate knowledge of mathematics content and pedagogy is essential for teachers to effectively address the needs of a diverse group of students. Teachers should regularly take advantage of the inservice opportunities that are content-specific professional development to enrich their content knowledge and to stay abreast of the latest teaching techniques.

The physical environment of the classroom should be interesting and inviting for all students. The classroom should display student work and other material that show a diverse group of people involved in mathematics activities and careers. The classroom arrangement should allow all members of the class to participate in mathematics activities regardless of their current achievement levels.

The focus of an equitable mathematics program must be on student outcomes. Teachers and principals are responsible for the achievement of all students, and consequences for lack of student success fall not only on students, but also on teachers, principals, the school, and the family.

References

Campbell, P., & Kreinberg, N. (1998). Moving into the mainstream: From equity as a separate concept to high quality includes all.

Comer, J. P. (1985). The Yale-New Haven Primary Prevention Project: A follow-up study.

Delgado, C. -G. (1991). Involving parents in the schools: A process of empowerment.

Edmonds, R. R., & Frederiksen, J. R. (1978). Search for effective schools: The identification and analysis of city schools that are instructionally effective for poor children.

National Research Council. (1989). Everybody counts: A report to the nation on the future of mathematics education.

Payne, R. K. (1998). A framework for understanding poverty.

Resnick, L., Bill, V., Lesgold, S., & Leer, M. (1991). Thinking in arithmetic class.

Secada, W. (1992). Race, ethnicity, social class, language and achievement in mathematics.

Tye, K. A. (1992). Restructuring our schools: Beyond the rhetoric.

U.S. Department of Labor. (1993). Learning a living: A blueprint for high performance (SCANS report).

Teaching

Assessment

Curriculum

Technology

Learning

What are the impacts of ability grouping and tracking on student learning?

As the demand for a more mathematically literate society grows, schools need to respond to this challenge and provide meaningful mathematics to all of our students, all of the time.

Research and Best Practice

The student should be the reference point for addressing the complex issue of who should learn what mathematics and when. The challenge of addressing diverse students' needs encourages us to reflect upon the implications of placing students in various ability groups or tracks for mathematics instruction. Research suggests that these practices do not provide the same educational experience for all students.

Studies suggest that expectations placed on students differ according to their assigned ability group or track. Students deemed less capable experience less depth and breadth in school mathematics. Indications are that the most experienced teachers are assigned to teach high-level classes, while teachers with the least experience and mathematical background are assigned to teach the lowest-performing students in mathematics. Studies also reveal crucial differences in the kinds of instruction offered in different tracks. Instruction in the lower tracks tends to be fragmented, often requiring mostly memorization of basic facts and algorithms and the filling out of worksheets. Although some higher track classes share these traits, they are more likely to offer opportunities for making sense of mathematics, including discussion, writing, and applying mathematics to real life situations.

Tracking and ability grouping rarely allow for upward movement between ability groups or tracks when a student makes some developmental leaps. Hence, a conflict exists between the structure of academic tracks or ability groups and the potential academic and intellectual growth of struggling students who may be late bloomers.

An alternative to homogeneous strategies of tracking or ability grouping is mixed ability or heterogeneous grouping for instruction. Heterogeneous instruction emphasizes a differentiated classroom approach, in which teachers diagnose student needs and design instruction based upon their understanding of mathematics content using a variety of instructional strategies that focus on essential concepts, principles, and skills.

Inherent in this practice is the opportunity for all students to receive quality mathematics instruction. As the demand for a more mathematically literate society continues, schools need to respond to this challenge and provide meaningful mathematics to all of our students, all of the time.

Mathematics
For All •

Mathematics For
All

Teaching

Assessment

Curriculum

Technology

Learning

Classroom Implications

To effectively teach students coming from a variety of previous mathematics learning experiences and successes, teachers should thoughtfully choose instructional strategies for working with de-tracked or heterogeneous groups. The teacher must believe that all students can learn, although in different ways and at different rates.

These instructional elements have been shown to be effective for mixed ability mathematics classes:

- A meaningful mathematics curriculum. This means providing contexts that give facts meaning, teaching concepts that matter, and framing lessons as complex problems.

- An emphasis on interactive endeavors that promote divergent thinking within a classroom. Students need to construct knowledge with peers, including safe and regular opportunities to take risks, exchange ideas, and revise their understanding of mathematics.

- Diversified instructional strategies that address the needs of all types of learners. To embrace multiple intelligences is to present information in a variety of ways.

- Assessment that is varied, ongoing, and embedded in instruction. Performance assessments, a portfolio of growth and achievements, projects demonstrating the accompanying mathematics, and solving and reporting on complex problems in varied contexts will provide evidence of student learning.

- Focused lesson planning that, instead of emphasizing what the classroom teacher wants to teach, begins by understanding what students need to learn (outcomes) and assessing what they already know.

Employing these techniques will provide a rich classroom experience and an effective way to enhance the learning of mathematics for all students.

References

Battista, M. T. (1994). Teacher beliefs and the reform movement in mathematics education.

Oakes, J. (1993). The tracking wars: Is anyone winning?

Tomlinson, C. A. (1999). The differentiated classroom: Responding to the needs of all learners.

Tsuruda, G. (1994). Putting it together: Middle school math in transition.

What can schools do to facilitate students' opportunity to learn mathematics?

Opportunity to learn is facilitated through student-centered classrooms that are focused on higher-order thinking skills, problem solving, substantive conversation, and real world contexts.

Research and Best Practice

A basic definition of opportunity to learn (OTL) is provision of access to learning, to which teachers serve as key gatekeepers. OTL components include being able to take needed courses, a curriculum that meets content standards and is free of hidden bias, time to cover content during school hours, teachers capable of implementing content standards, adequate educational resources, respect for diversity, and ancillary services to meet the mental and social welfare needs of all students.

Learning is an active process that allows students the opportunity to construct understanding through empirical investigation and group interaction. Opportunity to learn is facilitated through student-centered classrooms that are focused on higher-order thinking skills, problem solving, substantive conversation, and real-world contexts. Learner-centered classrooms engage students in social and interactive mathematical inquiry accomplished through evidence-based discussion and reflection on learning.

Opportunity to learn is enhanced by linking student learning to their social and cultural identity, which assists students to better understand the subject being taught. The premise of culturally responsive curriculum and pedagogy is that a student becomes more engaged in mathematical content when that content is significant to cultural beliefs and values. Using a context with which students are already familiar and incorporating a variety of role models amplifies students' confidence and comfort with the content being taught. These strategies demonstrate that everyone can be successful in mathematics.

While other staff, such as school counselors, play important roles in facilitating OTL, it is mainly the teacher who assures that opportunities exist. Students of teachers who majored or minored in mathematics achieve at a higher level than those whose teachers are less prepared. Teachers' attitudes and expectations can affect student achievement by increasing or decreasing students' effort and performance. By varying instruction, understanding the differences in needs and learning styles of individual students, and fostering discourse, teachers facilitate the development of learning communities. A community learning climate improves student achievement. Inclusive climate depends heavily on access to a rich array of learning resources and manipulative materials. This environment promotes group collaboration, and is essential to student-centered classrooms.

Mathematics
For All •

Mathematics For All

Teaching

Assessment

Curriculum

Technology

Learning

Classroom Implications

Skilled and qualified teachers, school counselors, administrators, and education policymakers can help all students achieve to their greatest potential. Their influence can convey high expectations and help raise students' self-esteem and performance. Administrators and policymakers can ensure that there are appropriately prepared teachers for all levels of instruction. Graduation requirements in mathematics should reflect the importance of knowledge of algebra, geometry, and higher mathematics in students' future careers. High school administrators can allow teachers adequate instructional time through appropriate class scheduling. Counselors' work with students in assigning classes must have as a goal appropriate higher-level mathematics coursework for all high school students. Elementary school administrators should emphasize the importance of allocating adequate daily instructional time for mathematics.

A standards-based curriculum implemented with the creative use of classroom strategies can provide a learning environment that both honors the mathematical strengths of all learners and nurtures the areas where students are most challenged. By including mathematics content from a variety of cultures and personal experiences, teachers enhance the learning experience for all students.

When instruction is anchored in the context of the learner's world, students are more likely to take ownership and determine direction for their own learning. Teachers, armed with opportunity-to-learn strategies, facilitate students' taking responsibility for their own learning, and the result is an equitable learning experience. Consequently, students' mathematical knowledge becomes connected to a socio-cultural context to create mathematical proficiencies.

To foster good mathematics teaching and high student achievement, adequate resources for classroom instruction should be made available to all students to promote high achievement. Students should use manipulatives, calculators, and computers for a rich variety of investigations. Schools that support equal access to mathematics supplies, equipment, and instructional resources are more likely to produce a student population with higher mathematical literacy.

References

Cuevas, G., & Driscoll, M. (Eds.). (1993). Reaching all students with mathematics.

Haycock, K. (1998, Fall). Good teaching matters ... a lot.

Michigan Department of Education, & North Central Regional Educational Laboratory. (1998). Connecting with the learner: An equity toolkit.

National Center for Education Statistics (2000). Pursuing excellence: Comparison of 8th grade mathematics and science achievement from a U.S. perspective, 1985 and 1999.

How can different learning styles be addressed with consistent expectations?

Research and Best Practice

Learning styles are collections of personal characteristics, strengths, and preferences describing how individuals acquire, store, and process information. Learning style factors include information processing modes, environmental and instructional preferences, cognitive capabilities, and personality features. Individuals might demonstrate a balance among the dimensions of a learning style, or they might show strengths and weaknesses. These strengths and weaknesses may have implications for course success and eventually for career choice. Groups of students from different cultures might exhibit distinct average learning styles, but there are often such broad within-group variations that generalizations about learning styles and cultural background are not valid.

"They're not dumb, they're different."
Tobias, S., 1999.

Learning styles not only influence how individuals learn, but also how they teach. Teachers often instruct in the same manner in which they were taught even if the teaching style does not support the learning style preferred by most students. Teachers aware of their own teaching styles are able to make better choices of instructional strategies that do not impede student learning. They can interpret students' questions, comments, and answers in the context of learning style variations. For collaborative group work, whole-brain multi-style student teams will optimize discussion and problem solving.

It is important for students to know their own learning style strengths and weaknesses and to develop a set of learning strategies to use their strengths and compensate for weaknesses. When instructed in the use of various learning strategies, students become more efficient and effective in their studying and more likely to attribute success or failure to their own choice of learning behavior rather than to their innate competency. Teachers who have taught their students about learning styles find that they learn the material better because they are more aware of their thinking processes. Students conscious of learning style differences develop interpersonal communication skills critical to adult success.

Longitudinal studies of outcomes of instruction specifically geared to a broad range of learning styles show students have more skill in applying knowledge, increased satisfaction with instruction, and enhanced self-confidence.

Classroom Implications

Learning style strengths and weaknesses can influence task success and overall achievement. Students should know personal learning strengths and weaknesses and be able to use their knowledge of these strengths to compensate for weaknesses. Tools for assessing learning (and teaching) styles are available. They can provide clues, not labels, to personal styles; learning styles are preferences, not traits or abilities. Students need to learn strategies for coping with varied learning environments and how to modify or generalize strategies for novel situations. Strategy use includes knowledge about the strategy, when to use it, and how to tell if it worked.

When there is a significant unaddressed mismatch between teaching and learning styles, students are inattentive, bored, or discouraged and often perform poorly. In response, teachers may become overly critical, misinterpret poor scores as low ability (which exacerbates the situation), or become discouraged with teaching. Therefore, teachers must know how to identify learning and teaching styles and how to teach students to use various learning strategies. They can use differentiated instruction that is varied enough to meet students' needs while respecting diversity. Choosing from among standards-based learning methods, tasks, products, and assessments benefits diverse learners.

If teachers teach exclusively in a student's less preferred style, discomfort can interfere with learning. However, students benefit from experience with non-preferred learning styles. Preferred styles are not static, and skill development in non-preferred modes provides advantageous mental dexterity. Learning in the early stages of a curriculum unit may be more efficient using a different style than later in the same unit. It is important that the teacher balance instructional methods so that all students are taught partly in their preferred styles, but also practice learning in less preferred modes. Teaching that addresses all dimensions ("teaching around the cycle") of one of the theoretical models is more effective than unidimensional teaching.

In assessing students whose learning will be demonstrated through different learning styles, it is important for the teacher to consider the criteria for success. Demonstrations may vary, depending on learning styles, but in a standards-based classroom, the expectations of content and process coverage can be met through any demonstration that addresses the standards.

References

Anderson, J., & Adams, M. (1992). Acknowledging the learning styles of diverse student populations: Implications for instructional design.

Armstrong, T. (1994). Multiple intelligences in the classroom.

Dunn, R. (1996). How to implement and supervise a learning style program.

Dunn, R., & Griggs, S. (1995). Multiculturalism and learning style: Teaching and counseling adolescents.

Felder, R. (1996). Matters of style.

Gardner, H. T. (1993). Multiple intelligences: The theory into practice.

McKeachie, W. (1995). Learning styles can become learning strategies.

Silver, H. F., Strong, R. W., & Perini, M. (2000). So each may learn: Integrating learning styles and multiple intelligences.

Spoon, J., & Schell, J. (1998). Aligning student learning styles with instructor teaching styles.

Tobias, S. (1990). They're not dumb, they're different: Stalking the second tier.

Tomlinson, C. A. (1999). The differentiated classroom: Responding to the needs of all learners.

Mathematics For All

Teaching

Assessment

Curriculum

Technology

Learning

Teaching Mathematics

Learning and teaching mathematics are both complex, active processes. Teachers are constantly making decisions as they facilitate a daily learning environment in which they work with their students as active learners. They must also undertake long-term planning to connect daily efforts into the total education of each student. At the same time, teachers share responsibility for their students' successes with other factors in the educational community, including their colleagues, their institutions, and the policies of the educational system.

The National Council of Teachers of Mathematics (NCTM) *Principles and Standards for School Mathematics* (*PSSM*) outlines theoretical and practical knowledge and understandings about mathematics, how children acquire mathematics content, and mathematics teaching techniques that facilitate each child's learning. Effective professional development moves teachers toward the goals spelled out in these professional standards for teaching mathematics. Because a teacher's classroom decisions affect the achievement of each student, teachers need to avail themselves of strategies that are as varied as their students and their educational needs.

What instructional methods support mathematical reasoning and problem solving?

Mathematical reasoning and problem solving requires teachers to teach mathematics as the power of thought rather than the power of discrete facts.

Research and Best Practice

Research on best instructional methods for teaching and learning mathematical reasoning and problem solving consistently and clearly identifies the necessity for teachers to provide mathematically rich environments conducive to investigations.

Effective mathematics instruction occurs in community settings in which teachers carefully select problems, materials, and grouping practices, provide opportunity for mathematics discourse, and use assessment practices designed to provoke and support student thinking. Mathematical reasoning and problem solving requires teachers to teach mathematics as the power of thought rather than the power of discrete facts.

Instructional methods that support and promote student sharing and active listening enhance student reasoning and problem solving skills. Instructional practice should promote explorations supported by easy access to a wide variety of tools that are designed to accomplish a task. The tools students use influence the kinds of understandings they develop.

Both mathematics and science have standards of proof: an argument must be supported by evidence, and conclusions must be logically derived. Through questions and clarifications, teachers guide student understanding, they follow the evolution of student thinking in order to guide it effectively, and at appropriate times — but not prematurely — they introduce current mathematical or scientific ideas.

Teachers who orchestrate the integration among conceptual, procedural, and factual knowledge provide the "sense making" that is necessary if students are to develop confidence in their ability to reason and solve problems.

Classroom Implications

Classrooms that promote mathematical reasoning and problem solving typically are supportive, collegial communities. Teachers make instructional choices which support the opportunity for all children to learn important mathematics. Teachers find ways to support students as they work through challenging tasks without taking over the process of thinking for them and thus eliminating the challenge.

An effective classroom model includes a structure in which teachers pose interesting, challenging problems or tasks to the class as a whole. Time is allotted for students to

- Individually ponder appropriate strategies
- Identify necessary tools to assist in solving the problem
- Work in small groups exploring and discussing ideas, and solving the problem
- Report their findings to the class

Students are challenged to approach a problem by using logic and powers of observation, reasoning, models, evidence, examples, and counterexamples to discover meaningful patterns. Opportunities are provided for students who solved the problem differently from other students to share their procedures, thus encouraging diverse thinking. Through classroom interactions, students are encouraged to develop mathematical ideas and conjectures and learn to evaluate their own thinking and that of others.

Effective instructional methods promote student activity such as

- Comparing and clarifying
- Analyzing information that leads to summarizing
- Creating graphic representations, drawing pictures and pictographs

Tools or manipulatives should be used as an integral resource and support for building understanding, but effective teachers recognize that the tools themselves do not provide meaning. Rather, they help students make connections. Emphasis on children doing meaningful mathematics is fostered by providing rich experiences with mathematics both inside and beyond the classroom.

References

Bransford, J. D., Brown, A. L., & Cocking, R. R. (Eds.). (1999). How people learn: Brain, mind, experience, and school.

Hiebert, J., Carpenter, T. P., Fennema, E., Fuson, K. C., Murray, H., Oliver, A., Human, P., & Wearne, D. (1997). Designing classrooms for learning mathematics with understanding.

Mokros, J., Russell, S. J., & Economopoulos, K. (1995). Beyond arithmetic: Changing mathematics in the elementary classroom.

Thompson, C., & Zeuli, J. (1999). The frame and the tapestry: Standards-based reform and professional development.

Mathematics For All

Teaching

Assessment

Curriculum

Technology

Learning

How is mathematical thinking addressed in the mathematics classroom?

> **"Being able to reason is essential to understanding mathematics."**
>
> National Council of Teachers of Mathematics, 2000, p. 56.

Research and Best Practice

Mathematical thinking embodies processes that are the actions of doing mathematics. It can be used as ways of acquiring and using content knowledge and skills. Mathematical processes include problem solving, mathematical reasoning and proof, communication, connections, and representation.

It was once believed that the ability to solve mathematical problems automatically derived from knowing the mathematics. For all mathematical processes, it has been found that in addition to having a well organized understanding of the mathematics involved, experience solving a wide variety of problems is necessary. Students need many opportunities to use mathematical processes.

Reasoning and proof are mathematical processes that relate closely to scientific inquiry. In the process of proof, mathematicians often start by testing with numbers, then look at some special cases and test again. From this they can formulate a hypothesis and try to deduce the final result. Mathematical reasoning also includes graphic and algebraic reasoning, proportional and probabilistic reasoning, and geometrical and statistical reasoning.

In the process of communicating their understanding of mathematics and trying to make their ideas understood, students amend and refine them. Communicating mathematics includes reading, writing, discourse, and using multiple representations. Definitions are important in mathematics, and students need to understand the role they play and use them in their mathematical work.

Connections among mathematical ideas help students build deeper understandings. Mathematics also connects with other subject areas and the real world, showing the power and practicality of mathematics. There are also connections between different ways that a mathematical idea can be represented.

Representations of mathematical ideas can be visual, including equations, graphs, pictures, and charts. Representations may be in the mind of the student as he or she interprets the mathematical situation. Students can also use verbal descriptions and examples to communicate their ideas and findings. Students' mental representations of problems affect how they go about solving them. Students with well-developed understandings of a concept can represent it in a variety of ways.

Classroom Implications

Selection of worthwhile mathematical tasks is important. These tasks should contain sound and significant mathematics, that rest on knowledge of students' understandings, interests, and experiences, and that capitalize on the range of ways that diverse students learn mathematics. Additionally, tasks need to be engaging; develop mathematical understandings and skills; call for connections and coherence, problem formulation, problem solving, and mathematical reasoning; promote communication; and stimulate students' dispositions to do mathematics.

Rich tasks are not enough. Teachers should ask

- Do the tasks lead anywhere?
- Do the tasks lead to model building?
- Do the tasks lead to inquiry and justification?
- Do the tasks involve flexible use of technologies?
- Are the tasks relevant to the students?

Reasoning skills need to be continually developed through curricula that build on students' existing knowledge, but that present disequilibrium or discrepancies that call for resolution and continuation of the development of knowledge.

Connection of mathematical ideas promotes understanding so that students can apply that knowledge to learn new topics and to solve unfamiliar problems. Understanding is developed through the construction of relationships, by extending and applying mathematical knowledge, by reflecting about experiences, by articulating what one knows, and by making mathematical knowledge pertinent to oneself. All processes imply making connections among these areas.

Representations support learning. Appropriate use of electronic technology has given representations an enhanced role in mathematics instruction. Tasks need to stimulate students to use various representations to model their mathematical thinking. Then students need to learn to translate between and among representations and to use those translations to continually augment their thinking.

References

Fennema, E., & Romberg, T. A. (Eds.). (1999). Mathematics classrooms that promote understanding.

Hiebert, J., Carpenter, T. P., Fennema, E., Fuson, K. C., Kearne, D., Murray, H., Olivier, A., & Human, P. (1997). Making sense: Teaching and learning mathematics with understanding.

National Council of Teachers of Mathematics. (1991). Professional teaching standards for school mathematics.

National Council of Teachers of Mathematics. (2000). Principles and standards for school mathematics.

Romberg, T., & Kaput, J. (1999). Mathematics worth teaching, mathematics worth understanding.

Mathematics for All

Teaching

Assessment

Curriculum

Technology

Learning

What role does teacher questioning play in learning mathematics?

Effective mathematics teachers ... ask many questions of all types during their lessons.

Research and Best Practice

Learning is maximized in classrooms where questions are encouraged, elaboration and explanation are expected, and feedback is frequent. In such classrooms, both large and small group discussions are prevalent, with interaction between teacher and students and among students.

Effective mathematics teachers (those who are highly rated by their students and whose students perform well on both content and problem-solving skills assessments) ask many questions of all types during their lessons. Compared to less effective teachers, they pose more questions with higher cognitive demand, and ask more follow-up questions. Their students ask more questions, as well. Effective teachers orchestrate productive discussion in classrooms. Students engaged in discussion are better able to make sense of ideas, create as well as demonstrate understanding, and reflect on their thinking. Questions can be used as an effective learning tool prior to a learning experience.

Students in high-performing and conceptually-oriented classrooms are expected to share ideas with others. Striving to explain their thinking helps students clarify their own ideas, even when their thinking is not totally clear, or their understanding is not well formulated. Students who must explain their thinking organize their thoughts differently, analyzing the strategies they employed by engaging in self-reflection and analysis.

Studies of questioning in typical mathematics classrooms confirm that most questions make minimal demands on student thinking. Low level questions include yes/no questions; guessing; simple recall of fact, formula, or procedure; leading or rhetorical questions; and those answered immediately by the teacher. Answers are often immediately judged right or wrong by the teacher, and discussion moves to the next question. Increasing the wait time between posing a question and expecting an answer increases the number of responses, student confidence, responses by less able students, and reflective responses.

Classroom Implications

Better teacher questioning practices lead to better learning by all students. The foundation of good questioning is strong content knowledge, which is a critical factor in enabling teachers to understand and respond appropriately to students' questions. In addition, teachers must have a firm understanding of how students learn topics so they can anticipate students' misunderstandings and plan appropriate questions.

Good questioning requires skill and planning. Strategies to improve questioning techniques include

- Plan questions while preparing lessons. Write out questions to launch a lesson, and compose clarifying questions to use during exploration.
- Choose different questions for varied purposes — clarifying questions, redirecting questions, summarizing questions, extension questions, and reflection questions.
- Tape lessons occasionally to monitor levels of questioning.
- Focus questions on searching for student understanding. Remove emphasis from right or wrong answers. Low-level questions do not give a good picture of a student's grasp of a concept.
- Listen carefully to student answers.
- Ask for a paraphrase of what has been said. This improves attentiveness and assesses comprehension.
- Assume that every answer given by a student is meaningful and "correct" to that student. The answers give insight into the student's mind by illuminating misconceptions and misunderstandings.
- Begin lessons with rich questions or problems to engage students and lead to new understanding of important content. Provide a variety of tools to assist mathematical exploration.
- Provide multiple opportunities for social interaction around mathematics ideas. People construct learning by questioning, discussion, and reflection.
- Allocate time carefully. Make notes from class to class on effective amounts of time for each explanation.
- Increase wait time. An observant teaching partner can assist.
- Model self-questioning by "acting out" your thinking when you approach a problem. "I wonder what I should do next? Maybe I should try ___."

References

Cawelti, G. (Ed.). (1999). Handbook of research on improving student achievement.

Corwin, R. B., Storeygard, J., &. Price, S. L. (1995). Talking mathematics: Supporting children's voices.

Elliott, P. C. (Ed.). (1990). Communication in mathematics: K–12 and beyond. 1990 yearbook.

Hiebert, J., Carpenter, T. P., Fennema, E., Fuson, K. C., Kearne, D., Murray, H., Olivier, A., & Human, P. (1997). Making sense: Teaching and learning mathematics with understanding.

Johnson, J. (2000). Teaching and learning mathematics: Using research to shift from the "yesterday" mind to the "tomorrow" mind.

National Council of Teachers of Mathematics. (1991). Professional teaching standards for school mathematics.

Suydam, M. N. (1985). Questions? Research report.

Yackel, E., Cobb, P., Wood, T., Wheatley, G., & Merkel, G. (1990). The importance of social interaction in children's construction of mathematical knowledge.

Mathematics For All

Teaching

Assessment

Curriculum

Technology

Learning

How can teachers motivate students to enjoy and want to learn mathematics?

Students will feel more capable in mathematics if they attribute success to their abilities and effort and if they feel their success is meaningful.

Research and Best Practice

Students' perceptions of how successful they are in mathematics influence their motivation toward mathematics. Student effort is dependent on expectations of success, on whether the task is considered to be of value, and on whether presentation of the task is engaging. The task must be challenging enough to compel attention but must offer a high likelihood of success given appropriate effort by the student. Students should be encouraged to attribute their successes to diligence and perseverance and their lack of success to insufficient effort, confusion, or poor choice of strategy — not to lack of ability.

Motivation toward learning mathematics is greatly influenced by teacher actions and attitudes. More successful teachers are more knowledgeable about mathematics and are commited to the success of all students. The classroom environment is important. Students need to engage in discourse where they listen to, respond to, and question the teacher and one another. Respect for ideas, ways of thinking, and mathematical dispositions needs to be a tenet of the exchanges. Students need to learn to make conjectures, to evaluate approaches and tools, to analyze strategies, and to present convincing arguments. An environment that allows for conceptual exploration and has space and tools for investigation helps students work at making sense of mathematics both independently and collaboratively. When students feel comfortable in taking intellectual risks, autonomy in task selection is validating.

Intrinsic motivation generally yields greater success than extrinsic incentives. Activities that build a rich understanding of mathematics increase intrinsic motivation; there is nothing as exciting as learning. If students value mathematics, they become more skillful, achieve at a higher level, are more persistent problem solvers, and exhibit greater confidence. Additionally, extrinsic motivations such as grades and social pressure, when tied to student values, can also have positive effects.

Interesting contexts stimulate learning and retention. Cooperative group interactions and social construction of knowledge contribute positively to student engagement and attainment. Multiple approaches that allow students of different learning dispositions to gain access to problems engage students. Students will feel more capable in mathematics if they attribute success to their abilities and effort and if they feel their success is meaningful, than if they attribute success to luck or external influences.

Mathematics
Teaching •

Mathematics for All
Teaching
Assessment
Curriculum
Technology
Learning

Classroom Implications

Awakening joy in learning is accomplished by creating a climate of choice, freedom from judgment, belief in each student's abilities, and knowledge that talent is expressed in many ways. Students need opportunities to satisfy their curiosities, test their imaginations, create, wonder, and invent. Classrooms that allow students to enjoy learning and encourage playfulness, vitality, sensitivity, humor, and joy are inviting and stimulating. Environments that allow students to approach mathematics in many ways — with manipulatives, technological tools, and hands-on activities — engage students' multiple intelligences.

Challenge and feedback are factors in maximizing brain growth. Too much or too little challenge causes students to give up or to be bored. Many factors of the learning environment provide challenge — time, materials, access, expectations, support, novelty, décor. Intellectual challenge is created through problem solving, critical thinking, relevant projects, and complex activities.

Opportunities to reflect allow learners to provide feedback to themselves. Teacher feedback influences students' motivations to do better work. Peer feedback that shows value and care helps students enjoy experiences more and allows students to assess their ideas as well as their behaviors. Feedback is most effective when it is specific, immediate, and gives the receiver a choice.

Emotion and attention are the processes our body uses to survive and face challenges. Internal and external environments are continually assessed to determine what's important and unimportant. Emotion provides a quick, general assessment of the situation. Attention brings focus to the things that seem important. Curricular considerations related to thriving in an educational environment include accepting and controlling our emotions (beliefs regarding mathematics), using activities that provide emotional context (are more easily recalled and remembered), avoiding emotional stress (mathematical confidence), recognizing the relationship between emotions and health (an exciting atmosphere), using metacognitive activities (talking about why a particular mathematical method was pursued), and using activities that promote social interaction (mathematics as a language).

References

Armstrong, T. (1998). Awakening genius in the classroom.

Jensen, E. (1998). Teaching with the brain in mind.

Marzano, R. J., Pickering, D. J., & Pollock, J. E. (2001). Classroom instruction that works: Research-based strategies for increasing student achievement.

Middleton, J. A., & Spanias, P. (1999). Motivation for achievement in mathematics: Findings, generalizations, and criticisms of the recent research.

National Council of Teachers of Mathematics. (1991). Professional teaching standards for school mathematics.

Sprenger, M. (1999). Learning and memory: The brain in action.

Sylwester, R. (1995). A celebration of neurons: An educator's guide to the human brain.

What instructional strategies make mathematics teaching more learner-centered?

"Almost all, who have ever fully understood arithmetic, have been obliged to learn it over again in their own way."

Colburn, W., 1821, p. 212.

Research and Best Practice

Student-centered teaching respects the diversity of learners and uses this diversity to enhance learning and achieve improved results. The American Psychological Association has developed 14 research-based, learner-centered principles that draw from a century of research on teaching and learning and reflect current best educational practices. Although the principles focus more on psychological factors primarily internal to the learner, the interactions of external environmental factors with internal factors is recognized. Among the cognitive and metacognitive factors cited are

- Learners link new information with existing knowledge
- Learners use metacognition to select and monitor mental processes

Among the motivational and affective factors is

- Teachers can influence motivation and effort toward learning

Among developmental and social factors are

- Learning is most effective when it matches developmental readiness
- Learning is a social activity

Among individual differences factors is

- Learning is more effective when instruction takes diversity into account

Effective teachers know their students well — their strengths and weaknesses, their interests and preferences — and plan instruction to challenge all learners to meet high standards. To do this, teachers must find ways to surface students' prior mathematics knowledge and misunderstandings so that knowledge gaps can be addressed, inconsistencies resolved, and understandings deepened. They must also learn about their students' backgrounds outside of school, so that mathematics instruction can be contextualized. Mathematics teachers must include development of metacognitive strategies and social and communication skills in their classroom goals. Effective teachers understand what students know and need to learn and then challenge and support them to learn it well.

Classroom Implications

Students learn by connecting new ideas to prior knowledge. Effective, student-centered instruction combines guided questioning with a set of experiences and lessons chosen to build upon the experiences and level of understanding that students already have. Strategies for accessing students' prior knowledge include K-W-L (What do you know? What do you want to know? What did you learn?), pre-tests, questioning, and journal writing. Teachers must help students come to view mathematics not as an isolated set of rules to be memorized, but as the connection of ideas, mathematical domains, and concepts.

Learner-centered instruction provides time for students to reflect and gain a deep understanding of mathematics. It offers opportunities for students to revisit ideas they have previously learned and to solve new problems. As students struggle to solve problems, the role of the teacher becomes one of active listening, clarification of issues, and probing student thinking. In promoting an inquiry approach to mathematical problem solving, effective questions teachers might include are: What would happen if? Can you do it another way? What are you thinking? Tell me more about that, and Why do you think that will work?

Approaching a problem in various ways, making and testing conjectures, and justifying the reasonableness of various solutions are critical factors in the development of mathematical understanding. Student-centered instruction actively engages students in the pursuit of that mathematical understanding. Effective instructional strategies engage students in interesting situations and meaningful problems that emphasize inquiry and the discovery of mathematical ideas.

In student-centered classrooms, teachers engage students in investigating a mathematical concept by posing an interesting and challenging problem that contains meaningful mathematical ideas and multiple potential pathways for reaching a solution. Students will use a variety of tools, including manipulatives, calculators, and computers, to explore mathematics concepts and make sense of them individually and as a group of learners.

References

American Psychological Association. (1997). Learner-centered psychological principles.

Colburn, W. (1821). Intellectual arithmetic, upon the inductive method of instruction.

Collins, A. M. (Ed.). (2000). So, what questions should I ask to further student understanding?

Dowker, A. (1992). Computational strategies of professional mathematicians.

Ma, L. (1999). Knowing and teaching elementary mathematics: Teachers' understanding of fundamental mathematics in China and the United States.

Mathematics For All

Teaching

Assessment

Curriculum

Technology

Learning

How does linking instruction and classroom assessment impact student learning?

Ongoing, embedded classroom assessment promotes student learning.

Research and Best Practice

Classroom assessment, an essential tool for supporting and monitoring student progress toward mathematics standards, should be aligned with instruction to achieve three important benefits. First, classroom assessment embedded within a unit reveals to teachers what individuals and groups of students know, understand, and can do with the material they are learning. One research study showed that teachers who used open-ended, embedded assessments also discovered the limitations in their own understanding of mathematical concepts, leading to an expressed need for targeted professional development.

Ongoing, embedded classroom assessment promotes student learning. International studies of mathematics instruction show assessment is used particularly skillfully to promote learning in Japan, where teachers often begin lessons with a challenging, unfamiliar problem that promotes understanding and application of mathematical knowledge as well as measures understanding. For assessment to promote learning, it should be accessible to students (that is, it must use the skills and knowledge already mastered) and contain valuable mathematics skills and content. One research study found that teachers who learned to incorporate open-ended assessment into their teaching were also more likely to emphasize meaning and understanding, encourage students' autonomy and persistence, and instruct students in higher-order cognitive strategies. Students whose teachers use open-ended assessment items have enhanced attitudes toward mathematics and perform better on high-stakes assessment items that are open-ended than do those whose teachers do not use this type of assessment.

Classroom assessment can help students monitor their own learning. When students know what is expected of them, through feedback and grading criteria, they are better able to keep track of their own mastery of the material. Expectations should be made clear to students, for example, through rubrics that are written at a developmentally-appropriate level. When students know what aspects of a skill or concept will be assessed (e.g., written communication of their problem-solving strategy), they are more likely to meet the scoring criteria.

Mathematics
Teaching •

Mathematics For All

Teaching

Assessment

Curriculum

Technology

Learning

Classroom Implications

Assessment aligned with instruction that takes place during a unit is called formative assessment. It informs teachers of student progress toward learning goals, allowing instruction to be modified as needed to improve achievement. Ongoing assessment may include informal conversations with and observations of students, open-ended problems that reveal students' understandings and misunderstandings, and traditional paper-and-pencil tests. Teachers should choose the type of assessment to use based upon learner and instructional needs. For example, knowing that students often omit finding common denominators in adding fractions aids instruction, whereas knowing that students can add fractions correctly is critical before progressing on to the next topic. Focusing on the understanding of mathematical concepts and procedures for solving problems requires that teachers become comfortable with not always having all the answers and with being open to students' discoveries of novel approaches and unique understanding of the material.

Open-ended, constructed-response problems are more likely than short-answer or multiple-choice items to incorporate both higher-order thinking and routine skills into their solutions. They require students to explore multiple solution strategies, organize information, apply knowledge, analyze, interpret, and communicate results. Another potential advantage of open-ended assessment is the integration of material related to several mathematics standards into one problem, including communication, reasoning, problem solving, and multiple content areas. These types of assessments encourage learning as well as measure progress toward learning goals.

Many types of assessment, including journaling and creating portfolios, involve student self-monitoring. Reflective self-assessment allows students to be more aware of their own learning and understand their personal learning strengths and weaknesses. This can improve communication of individual needs with the teacher, who can better understand student efforts and attitudes through examination of the results of these self-assessments. Self-assessment thus serves a personal metacognitive goal of monitoring individual progress as well as a group goal of improving instruction.

References

Glatthorn, A. (1998). Performance assessment and standards-based curricula: The achievement cycle.

Marzano, R. J., & Kendall, J. S. (1996). A comprehensive guide to designing standards-based districts, schools, and classrooms.

National Council of Teachers of Mathematics. (1995). Assessment standards for school mathematics.

National Research Council (1993). Measuring what counts: A conceptual guide for mathematics assessment.

Stepanek, J., & Jarrett, D. (1997). Assessment strategies to inform science and mathematics instruction. It's just good teaching series.

Stigler, J. W., & Hiebert, J. (1999). The teaching gap: Best ideas from the world's teachers for improving education in the classroom.

How does teacher content knowledge impact instruction?

Mathematics teachers with deep knowledge of mathematics content are able to teach rich mathematical content to all students.

Research and Best Practice

Teachers need a deep understanding of the mathematics they teach — concepts, practices, principles, representations, and applications — to support effective instruction. A teacher's conceptual understanding of mathematics affects classroom instruction in a direct and positive way. Content knowledge influences the decisions teachers make about classroom instruction.

Differences between teachers who have a rich background in mathematics and those who do not are very evident in their teaching styles. When they possess explicit and well-integrated content knowledge, teachers feel free to teach dynamically with many representations of the same concept. Student comments and questions are encouraged. Teachers with more limited content knowledge may depend too heavily on textbooks for explanations of mathematical principles. This often results in controlled classroom environments in which students work individually at seatwork, with mathematics portrayed as a set of static facts and procedures.

A close examination of mathematics teaching styles has revealed that teachers with less content knowledge more often emphasize algorithms and procedures in mathematics class. Although teachers with deeper content knowledge teach these same skills to their students, they also engage them in forming a conceptual understanding of mathematics. When students understand the concepts of mathematics, they are better able to use mathematics successfully and demonstrate higher achievement on assessments.

While teachers need deep content knowledge in the domain of mathematics, they must also be familiar with common misunderstandings students have about mathematical concepts. Their own mathematics knowledge should be deep enough to help them anticipate these misunderstandings, such as confusing the least common multiple with the greatest common factor. They will use their knowledge of mathematics to be able to clarify mathematical concepts during instruction and to recognize students' valid alternative problem-solving methods and solutions.

Classroom Implications

Ideally, secondary teachers of mathematics should have a degree in mathematics, and all mathematics teachers should have a deep understanding of mathematics content. Additional teacher preparation courses should focus on those pedagogical methods that are most effective for building mathematical concepts in children such as teaching with manipulatives, letting students work collaboratively to solve problems, representing mathematics concepts in a variety of ways, and linking mathematics to other content areas.

Mathematics teachers with deep knowledge of mathematics content are able to teach rich mathematical content to all students. They can analyze student work for evidence of conceptual misunderstandings. Content knowledge allows mathematics teachers to

- Present mathematics topics in the context in which they occur in daily life
- Model mathematical content in a word-problem format so students will become accustomed to the way mathematics is commonly encountered in the real world
- Link mathematics to other content areas
- Relate learning mathematics to an understanding of technology, personal and social perspectives, historical issues, and cultural values

Skilled mathematics teachers use their knowledge to help students attain a deep understanding of mathematics concepts through activities with manipulatives. They encourage the strategic use of calculators and computers so that students can spend more time working higher-order problems, and they encourage students to participate in mathematical games. These teachers give students opportunities to use mathematics to answer real questions. They develop students' abilities to estimate and to evaluate the reasonableness of answers.

Students in these classes work on problems in groups so they can share their strategies. They explain their mathematical reasoning, both orally and in writing, and have opportunities to write their own problems.

References

Brophy, J. E. (1991). Conclusions to advances in research on teaching. Volume 2: Teachers' knowledge of subject matter as it relates to their teaching practice.

Fennema, E., & Franke, M. L. (1992). Teachers' knowledge and its impact.

Ma, L. (1999). Knowing and teaching elementary mathematics: Teachers' understanding of fundamental mathematics in China and the United States.

National Commission on Mathematics and Science Teaching for the 21st Century. (2000). Before it's too late: A report to the nation from the National Commission on Mathematics and Science Teaching for the 21st Century.

National Council of Teachers of Mathematics. (2000). Principles and standards for school mathematics.

Mathematics For All

Teaching

Assessment

Curriculum

Technology

Learning

How does teacher pedagogical knowledge impact instruction?

As teachers' pedagogical content knowledge increases within the context of a strong knowledge of mathematical content, their ability to impact student learning also increases.

Research and Best Practice

Pedagogical knowledge means understanding the methods and strategies of teaching. Specific methods or strategies that have been proven to work well in one content area, such as mathematics, are referred to as pedagogical content knowledge. According to the NCTM *Principles and Standards for School Mathematics*, "[e]ffective teaching requires knowing and understanding mathematics, students as learners, and pedagogical strategies." (p. 17)

The most direct route to improving mathematics achievement for all students is through better mathematics teaching. However, despite significant changes throughout society over the last half century, teaching methods in most mathematics classes have remained virtually unchanged. Many mathematics students spend much of their time on basic computational skills rather than engaging in mathematically rich problem-solving experiences.

Student knowledge improves substantially when teachers have strong content and pedagogical knowledge. Strong teacher content knowledge alone does not increase student knowledge. Neither does the use of effective pedagogical methods without adequate content knowledge improve student achievement substantially, and in some cases it may actually reinforce student misconceptions.

Extensive research has focused on the influence of teacher characteristics (educational background, years of experience), professional development (training to support classroom practices), and classroom practices (such as the use of small-group instruction or hands-on learning) on student achievement. Research shows that while all three components influence student achievement, the most influential factor is classroom practices.

Common mathematics teaching strategies, such as the use of worksheets and a heavy emphasis on computational fluency, are not as effective as engaging students in higher-order thinking skills and hands-on learning activities. Professional development tailored to increase teacher repertoires of classroom instructional practices — coupled with knowledge of mathematics content — increases student academic performance.

Classroom Implications

Effective mathematics teachers employ a large repertoire of instructional methods, strategies, and models to produce more successful learners. Different instructional methods accomplish different learning goals for different students. Teachers should carefully select and plan classroom experiences to provide meaningful mathematics learning opportunities for their increasingly diverse student population.

Highly effective mathematics teachers

- Have a deep knowledge of subject matter, which enables them to draw on that knowledge with flexibility
- Encourage all students to learn for understanding
- Foster healthy skepticism
- Allow for, recognize, and build on differences in learning styles, multiple intelligences, and abilities
- Carefully align curriculum, assessment, and high standards
- Conduct interim assessments of students' progress and use the results to improve instruction
- Measure instructional effectiveness through student performance and achievement
- Use a problem-solving approach

Contrary to the idea that the ability to teach is innate, specific teaching skills can be acquired through training, mentoring, collaborating with peers, and practice. To change the way they teach, mathematics teachers must be provided with first-hand opportunities to learn in different ways. They need to observe, practice, and refine high-quality teaching to master the art of teaching mathematics well. As teachers' pedagogical content knowledge increases within the context of a strong knowledge of mathematical content, their ability to impact student learning also increases.

References

Ma, L. (1999). Knowing and teaching elementary mathematics: Teachers' understanding of fundamental mathematics in China and the United States.

National Commission on Mathematics and Science Teaching for the 21st Century. (2000). Before it's too late: A report to the nation from the National Commission on Mathematics and Science Teaching for the 21st Century.

National Council of Teachers of Mathematics. (2000). Principles and standards for school mathematics.

National Council of Teachers of Mathematics. (1991). Professional teaching standards for school mathematics.

Wenglinsky, H. (2000). How teaching matters: Bringing the classroom back into discussions of teacher quality.

Mathematics For All

Teaching

Assessment

Curriculum

Technology

Learning

How do teacher attitudes about mathematics learning impact student achievement?

Teacher attitudes impact their daily choices of activities, the amount of effort expended on each, and their expectations of students' abilities to perform.

Research and Best Practice

Educational change depends on what teachers do and think, as does the success or failure of the educational process. Teachers mediate between the learner and the subject to be learned; consequently, teachers' beliefs, attitudes, and expectations have a major impact on student achievement.

Teacher attitudes impact their daily choices of activities, the amount of effort expended on each, and their expectations of students' abilities to perform. Teachers who believe it is important for students to learn mathematics with understanding embrace the use of investigations, mathematical discourse, and appropriate mathematical notation and vocabulary. Because a teacher's beliefs influence his or her instructional decisions, pedagogical choices will differ among teachers, yielding varied student achievement results. A teacher's belief in a blend of whole class, individual work, and small-group work on challenging and interesting problems results in improved student achievement.

Teachers who believe in the importance of providing all students the opportunity to learn mathematics with understanding employ strategies that promote student engagement in problem solving. They encourage students to make, test, and revise conjectures, and to support their reasoning with evidence. In contrast, teachers who believe that computational prowess is the most important component of mathematics typically demonstrate procedures and provide students time in which to practice those steps. Students who experience a problem-solving approach to the teaching and learning of mathematics consistently outperform students in classrooms that focus on skills and procedures.

Classroom Implications

Teachers' decisions and actions in the classroom directly affect how students will learn mathematics. Teachers need to understand the big ideas of mathematics and be able to represent mathematics as a coherent and connected enterprise.

Student attitudes toward mathematics correlate strongly with their mathematics teacher's ability to clarify concepts and generate a sense of continuity between the mathematics topics in the curriculum. Effective mathematics teachers approach the content from a more holistic level of understanding. The development of students' positive attitudes in mathematics is directly linked to their participation in activities that involve both quality mathematics and communication within the classroom. Students who have positive interactions with their mathematics teachers tend to have high confidence in their ability to do mathematics.

The attitude of the mathematics teacher is a critical ingredient in building an environment that promotes problem solving and makes students feel comfortable talking about mathematics. Teacher feedback is an important factor in mathematics learning. Students who perceive the teacher's feedback as being "informational" and useful for improving their competence will increase their intrinsic motivation to learn mathematics.

While some mathematics teachers have beliefs, attitudes, and expectations that will positively affect their students' learning and achievement, others will need to change in order for their students to appreciate and understand mathematics. Therefore, specific professional development experiences need to be designed for these teachers that start with examining the impact of teacher beliefs, attitudes, and expectations on learning and achievement. It should include a self-examination, and incorporate continuing mentoring and support.

References

Bandura, A., & Adams, N. E. (1977). Analysis of self-efficacy theory of behavioral change.

Darling, L. -H. (1994). National standards and assessments: Will they improve education?

Fullan, M. G. (1991). The new meaning of educational change.

National Council of Teachers of Mathematics. (2000). Principles and standards for school mathematics.

Reese, C. M., Miller, K. E., Mazzeo, J., & Dossey, J. A. (1997). NAEP 1996 mathematics report card for the nation and states.

Stigler, J. W., & Hiebert, J. (1999). The teaching gap: Best ideas from the world's teachers for improving education in the classroom.

Thompson, C., & Zeuli, J. (1999). The frame and the tapestry: Standards-based reform and professional development.

Mathematics For All

Teaching

Assessment

Curriculum

Technology

Learning

What are the characteristics of effective professional development for mathematics?

"Much of what constitutes the typical approach to formal teacher professional development is antithetical to what promotes teacher learning."

Bransford, J. D., Brown, A. L., & Cocking, R. R., 1999, p. 240.

Research and Best Practice

Improving teacher quality is the key to increasing student learning. In the past, teacher training transmitted discrete skills and techniques to participants who were then expected to deliver content to students. Research clearly shows that professional development for educators must be of adequate duration and must address subject matter and teaching methods to be effective.

A growing consensus about effective professional development is that it is most powerful when embedded in the daily work life of teachers to create a collaborative culture of inquiry about student understanding. In this environment, teachers learn new content and related teaching practices, apply them in the classroom, then reflect on the results.

In this approach to professional development, teacher dialogue about teaching and learning is guided by

- What state and national standards identify as the most important content and strategies for student learning
- Collected data (e.g., performance assessment, student observation, student interviews, standardized test results) about student learning
- Their own inquiries (e.g., action research, study groups) about improved practice

In this way, teachers build professional communities, reduce professional isolation, and remake their professional culture. The most effective schools have strong professional communities, characterized by ongoing collegial and collaborative inquiry into practice. Many U.S. schools are not structured for teachers to learn. However, schools that demonstrate continuing improvement in classroom practice focus on teacher learning within the context of a professional community.

Teaching improves in schools that transform themselves into cultures of collegiality, experimentation, and risk-taking. In some districts, professional development schools are providing opportunities for expert, novice, and preservice teachers, university faculty, and teacher leaders to collaboratively study teaching and learning. In this setting, school and university educators work as partners to improve classroom practices.

Classroom Implications

Effective professional development strategies help teachers work collaboratively to reflect on practice within a collegial culture. The five major purposes of professional development for teachers are (1) developing awareness, (2) building knowledge, (3) translating knowledge into practice, (4) practicing teaching, and (5) reflection. Different strategies address one or more of these different purposes:

- Immersion in mathematics: engaging in solving mathematics problems as learners
- Study groups: engaging in regular collaborative interactions around topics identified by the group to examine new information, reflect on classroom practice, and analyze data
- Case discussions: discussing problems and issues illustrated in written narratives or videotapes of classroom events
- Examining student work: looking at student products to understand their thinking so that appropriate instructional strategies and materials can be identified (Scoring assessments can lead to the same outcome.)
- Action research: looking at one's own teaching and student products learning through a classroom research project
- Curriculum implementation: learning, using, and refining specific curriculum materials to build understanding
- Curriculum development and adaptation: creating new instructional materials and strategies or adapting existing ones to better meet the learning needs of students
- Coaching and mentoring: working regularly with another teacher at the same or greater level of expertise to improve teaching and learning
- Lesson study: designing, implementing, testing, and improving one or several lessons over long periods, ranging from several months to a year

In order to engage in this kind of professional development, teachers need administrator support, time to work with colleagues, and access to resources, such as research and outside expertise. For teacher learning and, therefore, student learning to become a priority, the structure of schools and the policies affecting them must address these needs.

References

Bransford, J. D., Brown, A. L., & Cocking, R. R. (Eds.). (1999). How people learn: Brain, mind, experience, and school.

Darling, L. -H. (Ed.). (1994). Professional development schools.

Eisenhower National Clearinghouse for Mathematics and Science Education. (1998). Ideas that work: Mathematics professional development.

Fennema, E., & Franke, M. L. (1992). Teachers' knowledge and its impact.

Garet, M. S., Porter, A. C., Desimone, L., & Birman, B. F. (2001). What makes professional development effective? Results from a national sample of teachers.

Loucks, S. -H., Hewson, P. W., Love, N., & Stiles, K. (Eds.). (1998). Designing professional development for teachers of science and mathematics.

McLaughlin, M. W., & Talbert, J. E. (1993). Contexts that matter for teaching and learning.

National Commission on Teaching and America's Future (1996). What matters most: Teaching for America's future.

Newmann, F. M., & Wehlage, G. G. (1995). Successful school restructuring: A report to the public and educators.

Sparks, D. (1992). Merging content knowledge and pedagogy: An interview with Lee Shulman.

Sparks, D., & Hirsh, S. (1997). A new vision for staff development.

Mathematics For All

Teaching

Assessment

Curriculum

Technology

Learning

Assessment *In Mathematics*

Assessment is a complex, systematic procedure for collecting and interpreting data. In education, assessment is the primary mechanism for feedback on the attainment of standards to students and teachers, as well as to parents, the school district, and the community. The National Council of Teachers of Mathematics (NCTM) recommends the use of multiple assessment methods. Since assessments communicate expectations, providing an operational definition of what is important, the NCTM *Principles and Standards for School Mathematics* (*PSSM*) promotes the inclusion of authentic assessments — exercises that closely approximate how mathematics is used in the real world.

The *PSSM* Assessment Principle also recommends measuring both student achievement and opportunity to learn. Interpreted together, this information assists educators and the community at large in assuring that all students can achieve to their potential. Opportunity to learn measures are important in interpreting both high-stakes individual assessments and international achievement comparisons.

What roles can assessment play in mathematics teaching and learning?

Learning to use evidence from multiple sources of assessment data can yield a more accurate picture of what students know and are able to do.

Research and Best Practice

Assessment has traditionally been used to evaluate student achievement and content area programs. New approaches to mathematics teaching have expanded the role of assessment to include monitoring student progress and making instructional decisions. Resesarch and professional mathematics organizations endorse the use of multiple and varied measures of assessment, such as performance-based assessment, teacher observations, interviews, student projects, portfolios, and presentations. Such alternative forms of assessment generate the information a teacher needs to determine what students are thinking, how they are reasoning, and what the next instructional steps should be.

Student learning improves when assessment is a regular part of classroom practice. Using open-ended, inquiry-based problems is a teacher's best chance to assess a student's level of understanding in mathematics classes. However, teachers tend to use alternative assessments only if the task reflects their own understanding of the content and they value the content knowledge that is being assessed.

National and state assessments have an influence on what teachers, administrators, and parents value in the classroom. Because of this, adjustments are made to teaching and curricula that reflect the format and characteristics of these assessments, even though the changes (e.g., focusing on multiple-choice or short-answer formats) are not always consistent with recommendations regarding measurement of student understanding. These standardized, norm-referenced assessments tend to favor formats which give the impression there is always one right answer, a stand that also conflicts with the best practices in assessment recognized by various professional mathematics organizations. Some assessments are being used for purposes for which they were not originally designed, and the data collected is being misapplied or misunderstood.

Classroom Implications

Assessment can help teachers plan curricula and guide daily instruction. A balanced or aligned curriculum has assessments that match what is taught. Seamless instruction and assessment improves student learning.

Types of assessments include

- Selected-response assessments like multiple choice, true-false, and matching, which usually assess procedural knowledge and factual information. If well-constructed they can assess complex understandings, but students cannot demonstrate all they know.
- Constructed-response assessments, which allow students to demonstrate their learning by choosing how to answer the question.
- Performance tasks which integrate concepts, skills, facts, reasoning, and problem solving, but require extra time to implement and score.
- Observations, checklists, interviews, and portfolios, which allow students to show the full range of their achievement and progress, can be especially appropriate for students with a language barrier.
- Standardized, norm-referenced tests, which suggest students' relative strengths and weaknesses across different content strands.

Rubrics, used with either constructed response or perfomrance assessments, describe levels of quality for skills, knowledge, and understandings being assessed in order to achieve consistency in judging the quality of performances. Communicating these expectations to students prior to tasks can promote quality work on the performance assessment. Rubrics developed jointly by teachers and students focus learning on understanding, conceptual development, and problem solving.

Analyzing student work helps teachers see the depth of students' thinking and pinpoints sources of error or misunderstanding. Professional development that helps teachers learn how to analyze and respond to unconventional, as well as typical, student work is important.

Teachers need to become more proficient in thoughtfully interpreting data from the various reference models of assessments (norm-referenced, criterion-referenced, and growth continuum). Learning to use evidence from multiple sources of assessment data can yield a more accurate picture of what students know and are able to do. The data can also help educators make decisions as to whether there is curricular alignment or if delivery of the content needs to be modified.

References

Johnson, J. (2000). Teaching and learning mathematics: Using research to shift from the "yesterday" mind to the "tomorrow" mind.

Joyner, J., & Bright, G. (1998). Focusing on classroom assessment.

National Council of Teachers of Mathematics. (1995). Assessment standards for school mathematics.

National Council of Teachers of Mathematics. (2000). Principles and standards for school mathematics.

National Research Council. (2000). Inquiry and the national science education standards: A guide for teaching and learning.

Peressini, D., & Webb, N. (1999). Analyzing mathematical reasoning in students' responses across multiple performance assessment tasks.

Mathematics For All

Teaching

Assessment

Curriculum

Technology

Learning

How can the use of varied assessments provide important evidence of learning?

Multiple sources of evidence yield a more comprehensive, ongoing picture of student learning and academic progress.

Research and Best Practice

Assessment should provide evidence about students' knowledge of mathematics. In order to do so, assessment must be congruent with state and local standards and be a good fit with the curriculum and instructional methods being used by the teacher. As teachers strive to help their students achieve mathematical literacy (learning for understanding and the ability to mathematize problem situations), they need information about how their students are progressing. This information is most helpful when it comes from a variety of sources, both formal and informal, and should measure progress in students' mathematical thinking.

Because each assessment strategy has strengths and weaknesses, using a wide variety of classroom assessments gives a better picture of student learning than any individual approach could alone. There has been a shift from multiple-choice, short-answer tests that measure skills and procedures, toward authentic tasks that measure mathematical thinking and the use of mathematics in context. Multiple sources of evidence yield a more comprehensive, ongoing picture of student learning and academic progress, facilitate the exchange of information between teacher and students, and can be communicated readily to other members of the school community.

When their achievement is assessed by multiple means, students assume more responsibility for their input into the classroom discourse and become more reflective. They learn to focus on listening more productively, on communicating more clearly, and on investigating more deeply. Using specific results to inform actions, students gain confidence in tackling mathematics problems and in analyzing strategies and solutions. Multiple assessment measures, coupled with students' and teachers' awareness of the importance of assessment to teaching and learning for understanding, can help foster a learning environment centered on continual growth. Ongoing feedback on student assessments with opportunities to revise work helps students gain a deeper understanding of mathematics.

Classroom Implications

Mathematics teachers need to discuss the importance of continuous assessment with students. Scoring criteria and models of exemplary work need to be given to students before they begin their tasks. When students and teachers collaboratively establish assessment as a tool to inform classroom progress, finding a variety of appropriate measures becomes an important component of the instructional process. This includes making appropriate accommodations for students with special learning needs.

Effective teachers use questioning, classroom observations, interviews, and conferences to facilitate instruction and to inform decision making. Careful questioning helps students scaffold knowledge, focus thinking, and dig deeper into understandings. Observations framed around students' grasp of mathematics concepts, their dispositions toward learning, their communication abilities, and their group work contributions help the teacher identify appropriate instructional strategies. Interviews yield individual insights into a problem, a way of thinking, an orientation to problem solving, and a uniqueness of approach. Conferencing allows students and teachers to reflect together on knowledge gained, current disposition toward mathematics, and goals to pursue.

Individual self-evaluation through reflection (e.g., a mathematics autobiography, goal setting, individual daily evaluations, chronicling of "ah-ha's," record keeping, journaling, and writing in mathematics) personalizes the activity for the student. Through writing, students learn to organize, to convey, to question, to conclude, and to defend — all mathematics thinking processes. Conversation with peers augments learning.

The use of multiple means of assessment allows students to diversify thinking and response patterns. Unique assessments congruent with conceptual understanding such as use of real-world problems, computer-based assessment of higher-order understandings and processes, critical evaluation of mathematical logic, and structured problem-solving tasks are stretching thinking about meaningful mathematics assessment. A wide variety of assessments can facilitate classroom focus on standards-based mathematics experiences. Therefore, teachers need to increase their repertoire of assessment strategies. Ongoing professional development in which teachers examine a variety of student work is a critical part of assessment.

References

Clarke, D. (1997). Constructive assessment in mathematics: Practical steps for classroom teachers.

Fennema, E., & Romberg, T. A. (Eds.). (1999). Mathematics classrooms that promote understanding.

Grunow, J. E. (2001). Planning curriculum in mathematics.

Kulm, G. (Ed.). (1990). Assessing higher order thinking in mathematics.

Stenmark, J. K. (Ed.). (1991). Mathematics assessment: Myths, models, good questions, and practical suggestions.

Zemelman, S., Daniels, H., & Hyde, A. (1998). Best practice: New standards for teaching and learning in America's schools.

Mathematics For All

Teaching

Assessment

Curriculum

Technology

Learning

How can mathematical thinking be assessed in the classroom?

In assessing applications and other problem-based contexts for doing mathematics, we need to be able to identify essential mathematics content that is embedded.

Research and Best Practice

Mathematical thinking can be defined as "a search for truth or knowledge" or "a systematic investigation of a matter of interest," that embodies the mathematical processes — problem solving, inquiry, reasoning and proof, communication, connections, and representation. These processes can be construed as ways of acquiring and using content knowledge.

Assessing understanding requires multiple measures, informal and formal, over the course of time, that pay particular attention to three levels of reasoning: reproduction, connections, and analysis. We need to use techniques that measure students'

- Use of mathematics to make sense of complex situations
- Work on extended investigations
- Ability to formulate and refine hypotheses, collect and organize information, explain a concept orally or in writing, and work with poorly defined problems or problems with more than one answer, similar to those in real life
- Use of mathematical processes in the context of many kinds of problems rather than in isolation
- Understanding or misunderstanding about mathematical concepts
- Ability to define and formulate problems, question possible solutions, and look at all possibilities
- Progress over time

Since we are striving to assess higher-order thinking, it is important to identify the components of the mathematical thinking processes. In assessing applications and other problem-based contexts for doing mathematics, we need to be able to identify essential mathematics content that is embedded and to have some idea about how the context and content interact with performance.

Mathematics For All

Teaching

Assessment

Curriculum

Technology

Learning

Classroom Implications

A task that is intended to assess mathematical processes should provide opportunities for students to tell about the mathematics they used, to explain why they proceeded as they did, to relate what they did to something they've done previously, and to communicate their ideas in a manner most appropriate to them — pictures, graphs, discussions, written reports, electronic displays, and so on.

Often, good instructional tasks also are effective assessment pieces. Assessment that enhances mathematics learning becomes a routine part of ongoing classroom activity rather than an interruption. Opportunities for informal assessment occur naturally in every lesson. Simple procedures like listening to students as they work, observing them, accumulating their work over time (portfolios), and interviewing them are some of the informal measures that can provide valuable information to students and to the teacher for instructional decision making.

Formal assessments for mathematics processes often come in the form of performance tasks or student-constructed response items. Performance tasks might include projects or investigations which students present to their classmates as presentations or displays. For example, students could be taken around their neighborhood and asked to find a mathematics problem and then create a display of the problem and its solution. Or students could prepare a slide show presentation on some aspect of the chapter they just studied or a problem they liked from the chapter. The teacher would determine the students use of mathematics and mathematics processes in both projects.

Student constructed response items allow students to show their solution processes and can include the requirement that they explain their thinking. Rubrics and scoring guides should be shared with students in advance to communicate expectations of the mathematical performance. It is crucial that the scoring guides and rubrics give students credit for their insight about a task, their reasoning, the clarity of their communication, and the appropriateness of their representations, as well as for the accuracy of their results.

References

Clarke, D. (1997). Constructive assessment in mathematics: Practical steps for classroom teachers.

Grunow, J. E. (1999). Using concept maps in a professional development program to assess and enhance teachers' understanding.

Kulm, G. (Ed.). (1990). Assessing higher order thinking in mathematics.

National Council of Teachers of Mathematics. (1995). Assessment standards for school mathematics.

Shafer, M., & Romberg, T. A. (1999). Assessment in classrooms that promote understanding.

Stenmark, J. K. (1989). Assessment alternatives in mathematics: An overview of assessment techniques that promote learning.

What do national/international assessments tell us about teaching and learning mathematics?

The curriculum of the United States has been characterized as lacking in rigor, focus, and coherence.

Research and Best Practice

The results of the Third International Mathematics and Science Study (TIMSS) show that American students are not performing at acceptable levels in mathematics compared with their counterparts in other countries. Less than one-third of American students' performances on the National Assessment of Educational Progress (NAEP) tests can be classified as "proficient" in mathematics.

Mathematical competency is necessary for the changing economy and workplace, to prepare an educated citizenry for democracy, and for national security. The National Commission on Mathematics and Science Teaching for the 21st Century investigated the problem of why students' performance in mathematics is unacceptable. The preparation our students now receive in mathematics is not at the "world class" level that was to have been achieved by the year 2000.

In national and international studies, the curriculum of the United States has been characterized as lacking in rigor, focus, and coherence. It does not promote a deep understanding of mathematics and covers too many topics. The United States has used indirect means to improve student performance and teaching rather than investigating the interplay of curriculum reform, accountability, effective instructional strategies, and collaborative analysis for improvement.

Disaggregated NAEP results are instructive. Gender differences were statistically insignificant except at grade 12 where males outperformed females in mathematics. This difference can probably be attributed to the fact that males tend to complete advanced courses at a higher rate than females. Significant performance differences exist across ethnic groups at all grade levels even though the scores for each ethnic group have increased over the years. Factors such as socioeconomic status, home environment, and educational opportunities must be considered when interpreting the achievement differences among ethnic groups.

Classroom Implications

The national and state standards can be instructive to school districts as they develop local standards, documents, and procedures. There is a need to limit the number of topics addressed without compromising the integrity of a demanding curriculum. Introduction of more complex topics earlier allows students to address gradually the underlying concepts of the rigorous content of algebra, geometry, discrete mathematics, and statistics. Attention to standards allows curriculum developers to create coherent, articulated curricular programs.

There is a connection between what is taught and how well it is taught. Student performance is increased when students are taught to seek conceptual understanding rather than simply to follow procedures. Lesson design needs to reflect effective instructional strategies and should relate the various mathematical strands. Students need to be encouraged by teachers, counselors, and parents to continue their study of mathematics throughout high school.

International comparisons indicate that the most powerful instrument for change in student performance is improved teaching. A highly effective level of teaching

- Requires a deep knowledge of the mathematics being taught, as well as an understanding of what is most important to learn and what is most difficult to understand
- Engages students not only in the computational aspects of mathematics, but also in its more meaningful conceptual aspects
- Involves problem solving as students learn and apply the lesson content
- Insists all students learn at high levels
- Demands high quality professional development opportunities to keep teachers current in content, pedagogy, and assessment
- Includes time to share with colleagues, which is critical in developing a learning community and professionalism among teachers

Ongoing planned professional development for teachers is needed to achieve the level of teaching described by these characteristics. Designers of professional development for U.S. teachers could benefit from studying models used in other countries.

References

Mid-Atlantic Eisenhower Regional Consortium. (1997). TIMSS eighth grade sourcebook.

National Center for Education Statistics. (2000). Pursuing excellence: Comparison of 8th grade mathematics and science achievement from a U.S. perspective, 1985 and 1999.

National Commission on Mathematics and Science Teaching for the 21st Century. (2000). Before it's too late: A report to the nation from the National Commission on Mathematics and Science Teaching for the 21st Century.

National Research Council (1999). Global perspective for local action: Using TIMSS to improve U.S. mathematics and science education.

O'Sullivan, C. Y., Reese, C. M., & Mazzeo, J. (1997). NAEP 1996 science report card for the nation and states.

The National Institute on Educational Governance, Finance, Policymaking, and Management, & Consortium for Policy Research in Education. (1998). Policy brief: What the Third International Mathematics and Science Study (TIMSS) means for systemic school improvement.

U.S. Department of Education. (1997). Attaining excellence: A TIMSS resource kit.

Mathematics For All

Teaching

Assessment

Curriculum

Technology

Learning

Mathematics *Curriculum*

The Content Standards in the National Council of Teachers of Mathematics (NCTM) *Principles and Standards for School Mathematics* (*PSSM*) define the content of instruction, outlining what every student should know and be able to do. It is the district curriculum, however, that describes how that content is organized. In addition, curriculum includes the emphases and perspectives placed on the content, creating a map for educators to use in designing classroom experiences for students.

Recognizing that the intent of content standards is to present a goal for all students, teachers must make curriculum decisions that accommodate a wide variety of learning styles, backgrounds, and interests. When educators use multiple means of addressing individual standards, all learners have an opportunity to access common content.

What is the importance of standards-based curricula in mathematics?

Standards are most visible in American classrooms as curriculum.

Research and Best Practice

Standards are a set of expectations for what students will learn. A standards-based curriculum arises from a given set of standards. It provides the details of how students should progress through a variety of learning experiences in order to meet those standards. The Curriculum Principle of *Principles and Standards for School Mathematics* states, "A curriculum is more than a collection of activities: it must be coherent, focused on important mathematics, and well articulated across the grades." (p. 14)

While many curriculum publishers have retrofitted their programs to align with national standards, the match is often not a good one. The American Association for the Advancement of Science found that most traditional textbook series fail to include all the content specified in the national mathematics standards. Some of the newer curriculum materials, developed to fulfill the expectations of the national standards, are more promising. They do a better job at incorporating both the content and the instructional approaches envisioned in the standards.

Extensive longitudinal studies show that the mathematics standards in many school districts in this country are not as rigorous as those in other countries. In international studies, American students are not achieving world-class mathematics standards. U.S. students rated average by their teachers may actually be performing at the basic level by international standards. Many high school graduates need remedial courses before attempting college-level mathematics; too many do not pass their beginning university courses.

The new curriculum programs based on national standards increase students' understanding of mathematics, but the manner in which these programs are used greatly influences results. Programs must be implemented as they were designed. Taking the recommended amount of time to work through the scope and sequence, teachers should use all of the essential features of standards-based programs defined in the *PSSM* Curriculum Principle. These essential features include classroom discourse, the presentation of mathematics skills in the context of problem solving, and the application of learning to real situations. Further research is needed to determine which of these features are most essential, and how they should be incorporated into teaching practice.

Classroom Implications

Standards are most visible in American classrooms as curriculum. Standards-based curricula are powerful means of implementing standards, but new procedures are needed for selecting curricula in a standards-based setting. Programs that embed skill development in problem solving, games, real world situations and other contexts are unfamiliar to many educators, and the path of skill development in such materials is not always obvious at a glance; a casual examination of such materials will not reveal their value. Teachers need opportunities to experience sample lessons themselves and to try out multiple lessons while monitoring student learning.

Teachers who previously felt effective using traditional practices will need reassurance during the implementation of a standards-based curriculum. They may have been more comfortable with a more direct instructional approach than with problem solving. Teachers who believe that skills are learned through repeated practice might be tempted to supplement a standards-based program with unrelated skills practice that may interfere with learning. Since one of the characteristics of standards-based learning is coherence, teachers will achieve the best results using such curricula as intended. Otherwise, students are at an unintended disadvantage.

Good materials will have built-in teacher support. Initial and ongoing professional development is crucial for teachers implementing standards-based curriculum. Students who have no opportunity to learn the important content in national and state standards cannot reach those standards. Classroom practice must also change to provide success for all in learning and using such content materials.

References

Anderson, R. (1996). Study of curriculum reform.

Cawelti, G. (Ed.). (1999). Handbook of research on improving student achievement.

Goldsmith, L. T., Mark, J., & Kantrov, I. (1998). Choosing a standards-based mathematics curriculum.

Hiebert, J. (1999). Relationship between research and the NCTM standards.

Hiebert, J., Carpenter, T. P., Fennema, E., Fuson, K. C., Kearne, D., Murray, H., Olivier, A., & Human, P. (1997). Making sense: Teaching and learning mathematics with understanding.

National Council of Teachers of Mathematics. (1989). Curriculum and evaluation standards for school mathematics.

National Council of Teachers of Mathematics. (1991). Professional teaching standards for school mathematics.

National Council of Teachers of Mathematics. (2000). Principles and standards for school mathematics.

Zemelman, S., Daniels, H., & Hyde, A. (1998). Best practice: New standards for teaching and learning in America's schools.

Mathematics For All

Teaching

Assessment

Curriculum

Technology

Learning

How do we determine what students should know and be able to do in mathematics?

PSSM is not a traditional laundry list of topics.

Research and Best Practice

There is a general consensus that mathematics is a "gatekeeper" discipline. Students who demonstrate proficiency in mathematics are more likely to take advanced courses in high school and to continue on to post-secondary education. The question of what mathematics all students should know and be able to do is, therefore, extremely significant. It was this question that led to the development of the National Council of Teachers of Mathematics *Curriculum and Evaluation Standards for School Mathematics* in 1989 and its 2000 revision, *Principles and Standards for School Mathematics* (*PSSM*). The standards in these documents reflect a consensus of the input received from thousands of mathematicians, mathematics educators, parents, business leaders, and teachers about what content and processes all students should know and be able to do to be mathematically literate.

PSSM is not a traditional laundry list of topics commonly found in the table of contents of mathematics texts; rather it identifies the "big ideas" in mathematics and how those concepts develop throughout the grade bands. The content areas in which all students must become proficient include: number and operations, algebra, geometry, measurement, and data analysis and probability. The process skills critical to achieving mathematics proficiency include: problem solving, reasoning and proof, communication, connections, and representation. Research indicates that when mathematics procedural skills are learned in the context of real-world content, students typically demonstrate a deeper understanding of mathematics than when those skills are practiced in isolation.

The standards also set an expectation that all students learn to value mathematics, become confident in their ability to do mathematics, become mathematical problem solvers, learn to communicate mathematically, and learn to reason mathematically. These mathematical habits of mind are applicable not only in using the content and procedures of mathematics, but in acting as a responsible citizen.

Classroom Implications

In a standards-based curriculum, teachers design learning experiences to enable all their students to reach the level of understanding or skill described by applicable standards. One area that demands more attention in mathematics is number sense — how numerical quantities are constructed and how they relate to each other. Students who build and test their own theories about numbers and their relationships begin to think mathematically and to look for and analyze patterns in mathematics. Additionally, students need to make estimates, check the reasonableness of their answers, and demonstrate computational fluency in problem solving.

Learning geometry incorporates concrete models, drawings, and dynamic software. Studying measurement provides opportunities to learn about other areas of mathematics, including number operations, geometric ideas, statistical concepts, and notions of functions. Data analysis and probability are essential for informed citizenship. All students must formulate questions that can be addressed with data and have opportunities to collect, organize, and display relevant data to answer those questions. Students should use data analysis and probability to connect mathematics to other subject areas in meaningful rather than contrived ways.

Students should use multiple representations, choosing the appropriate representation for a particular problem situation. All students should be engaged in algebraic reasoning, not just manipulating symbols, but actively generating data, representing it in tables, charts, and/or graphs, identifying patterns and relationships, making predictions based on representations, and expressing relationships using symbols.

An effective investigative mathematics classroom resembles a laboratory. Classroom experiences should promote the development of students' reasoning, justification, and mathematics content skills. Students should be encouraged to use geometric representations for numeric and algebraic concepts, make and test conjectures, and be able to construct their own proofs.

References

Collins, A. M. (2000). Yours is not to reason why, just plug in the numbers and multiply.

Ferrini, J. G. -M., Johnson, L., & Mills, G. (Eds.). (1998). Making change in mathematics education: Learning from the field.

Mokros, J., Russell, S. J., & Economopoulos, K. (1995). Beyond arithmetic: Changing mathematics in the elementary classroom.

National Council of Teachers of Mathematics. (1989). Curriculum and evaluation standards for school mathematics.

National Council of Teachers of Mathematics. (2000). Principles and standards for school mathematics.

Porter, A. (1994). National standards and school improvement in the 1990's: Issues and promise.

Stevenson, H. W., & Stigler, J. W. (1992). The learning gap: Why our schools are failing and what we can learn from Japanese and Chinese education.

Mathematics For All

Teaching

Assessment

Curriculum

Technology

Learning

What is curriculum coherence and articulation?

A coherent curriculum effectively organizes and integrates important mathematical ideas. . . . Articulation ensures that there are connections.

Research and Best Practice

Principles and Standards for School Mathematics indicates that a curriculumis more than a collection of activities; it must be coherent, focused on important mathematics, and well articulated across the grades. An effective mathematics curriculum focuses on mathematics that will prepare students for continued study and for solving problems in a variety of school, home, and work settings.

Mathematics comprises different topical strands, such as algebra and geometry, but the strands are highly interconnected. The interconnections should be displayed prominently in the curriculum and in instructional materials and lessons. A coherent curriculum effectively organizes and integrates important mathematical ideas so that students can see how the ideas build on, or connect with, other ideas, thus enabling them to develop new understandings and skills.

Articulation describes the relationships among various elements in a curriculum. Articulation ensures that there are connections between lessons, units, courses, and grade levels, and that the connections make possible the increasingly rigorous development of ideas. A well-articulated curriculum challenges students to learn increasingly more sophisticated mathematical ideas as they continue their studies.

The Third International Mathematics and Science Study shows that most mathematics curricula in the U.S. lack coherence and focus. Comparing U.S. textbooks and curriculum guides with those of other countries shows that U.S. textbooks contain considerably more topics. Covering so many topics results in instruction that yields disjointed rather than coherent learning. This does not allow students to develop a deep understanding of the topics covered.

Examining the curricula used across the entire 13-year instructional span for coherence and articulation defined through standards in use by local school districts is an important way to improve the quality of education.

Classroom Implications

Several common practices contribute to a lack of coherence and articulation within a curriculum. These include

- Emphasis on mastery, using reteaching and repetition
- Use of rote memorization
- Content "coverage" by textbooks
- Overly flexible, modular curriculum design which promotes inconsistent instruction
- Lack of district attention to curriculum program development

To achieve coherence and articulation, a curriculum program must

- Focus on the concepts and skills that are critical to the understanding of important processes and relationships that can be developed over several age levels
- Help students develop an understanding of these concepts and skills over several years in ways that are logical and that reflect intellectual readiness
- Establish explicit connections among the concepts and skills in ways that allow students to understand both ideas and the connections among them
- Assess and diagnose what students understand to determine the next steps in instruction

A coherent curriculum will typically contain fewer topics, although the topics will be richer and lead to greater depth and persistence of understanding. Content must be presented to students at an age when they have a readiness for it, are capable of understanding it, and can see the relationships among ideas. A well-articulated, coherent curriculum program not only is designed to take advantage of important prior knowledge but to have multiple entry points that allow all students who may have gaps in their prior knowledge to participate and learn rigorous mathematics content.

References

Apthorp, H. S., Bodrova, E., Dean, C. B., & Florian, J. E. (2001). Noteworthy perspectives. Teaching to the core: Reading, writing, and mathematics.

Hoffman, K. M., & Stage, E. K. (1993). Science for all students.

National Council of Teachers of Mathematics. (2000). Principles and standards for school mathematics.

National Research Council. (1999). A guide for designing coherent curriculum programs in mathematics and science.

National Research Council. (1999). Designing mathematics or science curriculum programs: A guide for using mathematics and science education standards.

Schmidt, W., & Valverde, G. (1998). Refocusing U.S. math and science education.

Tyson, H. (1997). Overcoming structural barriers to good textbooks.

Mathematics For All

Teaching

Assessment

Curriculum

Technology

Learning

What is the importance of reading and writing in the mathematics curriculum?

Reading and writing activities can help students analyze, interpret, and communicate mathematical ideas.

Research and Best Practice

Reading, writing, and mathematics are, or should be, inseparable. Hands-on mathematics can stimulate curiosity, engage student interest, and build important prior knowledge before students read or write about the topic. The more students know about a topic, the better they comprehend and learn from text on the topic. Prior knowledge is the strongest predictor of student ability to make inferences from text.

Hands-on mathematics, though, must be combined with minds-on activities. Reading and writing activities can help students analyze, interpret, and communicate mathematical ideas. These are skills needed to evaluate sources of information and the validity of the information itself, a key competency for mathematically literate citizens.

Many of the process skills needed for mathematics are similar to reading skills, and when taught together would reinforce each other. Examples of common skills are predicting, inferring, communicating, comparing and contrasting, and recognizing cause and effect relationships. Teachers who recognize the interrelatedness of mathematics and literacy processes can design instruction that reflects these similarities. *Becoming a Nation of Readers* suggests that the most logical place for instruction in most reading and thinking strategies is in the content areas rather than in separate lessons about reading.

The importance of writing in the mathematics classroom cannot be overemphasized. In the process of writing, students clarify their own understanding of mathematics and hone their communication skills. They must organize their ideas and thoughts more logically and structure their conclusions in a more coherent way. Competency in writing can only be accomplished through active practice; solving mathematics problems is a natural vehicle for increasing students' writing competence.

Classroom Implications

Motivating and engaging students to speak, ask questions, learn new vocabulary, and write down their thoughts comes easily when they are curious, exploring, and engaged in their own mathematics inquiry. Teachers can take advantage of students' innate wonder and inquisitiveness to develop language skills while learning mathematics concepts. Integrating literacy activities into mathematics classes helps clarify concepts and can make mathematics more meaningful and interesting. Teachers can use a wide variety of literature, including trade books, texts, and fiction. Selecting a fiction book with a mathematical theme both provides information and captivates student interest. Fiction works successfully with young learners by embedding cognitive learning in imaginative stories.

Asking students to write mathematics journals about their problem-solving experiences or to articulate and defend their views about mathematics-related issues provides opportunities to clarify their thinking and develop communications skills. Other ways to integrate writing in mathematics are recording and describing situations that involve mathematics, or writing persuasive letters on social issues like the use of sampling by the Census Bureau. NCTM provides annual lists of outstanding new literature and multimedia materials.

For English language learners, instruction in mathematics can be enhanced by the use of hands-on materials. Interacting with materials and phenomena enables English language learners to ask and answer questions of the materials themselves and use the materials as visual aids in conversation with the teacher and peers. Visual and auditory clues should be plentiful — charts with pictures of materials and key procedures, for example. Teachers should select vocabulary carefully, repeat key words often, and refer to charts with the written words. Work in pairs or small groups makes native language support by peers or instructional aides more feasible.

Mathematics teachers can help all students increase their comprehension of mathematics texts by activating their prior knowledge through brainstorming, discussing the topic, asking questions, and providing analogies. Specific attention to vocabulary is often necessary to enable comprehension of mathematics texts. Teachers should introduce new vocabulary and use a graphic organizer, concept or semantic map, or collaborative peer study techniques to develop understanding of new words.

References

Anderson, R. C., Hiebert, E. H., Scott, J. A., & Wilkinson, I. A. G. (1984). Becoming a nation of readers: The report of the Commission on Reading.

Barton, M. L., & Heidema, C. (2002). Teaching reading in mathematics.

Billmeyer, R., & Barton, M. L. (1998). Teaching reading in the content areas.

National Commission of Excellence in Education. (1983). A nation at risk: The imperative for educational reform.

Mathematics For All

Teaching

Assessment

Curriculum

Technology

Learning

What are the most important considerations in selecting textbooks and other materials?

Given the relationship of the quality of the instructional materials to student achievement, it is important to pay sufficient attention to the selection of quality materials.

Research and Best Practice

Instructional materials for K–12 school mathematics include textbooks, manipulative sets, software, CDs, trade books and other multimedia materials. They are a primary source of classroom mathematics learning and also play a profound role in the education of teachers, since professional development is often structured around these materials. The process used to select mathematics materials is critical to providing students and teachers with a solid foundation for improving achievement.

Four key steps in the process of selecting instructional materials for mathematics education are

1. establishing a review/selection committee
2. determining selection criteria
3. selecting an evaluation instrument
4. evaluating and selecting materials

The process may be done at the district, school, department, or even the classroom level. Most decisions must be ratified by an administrator or school board. Many states review materials and restrict districts and schools to choosing among approved materials.

In a school or district with mathematics standards in place, the most important selection criterion is that instructional materials develop the student understanding called for in the standards. Quality instructional materials will enhance student understanding; promote students' active involvement; hold high expectations for all students, with guidance for teaching diverse learners; incorporate problem-solving skills; use an appropriate learning sequence; include assessment instruments and methods; and reflect current research in mathematics education. Reviewers familiar with the discipline and the standards must carefully study both content and instruction. When standards exist, the relevant content must be present or the materials should not be used.

Because the quality of the instructional materials is related to student achievement, it is important to pay sufficient attention to materials selection. The capacity to recognize high-quality materials can be developed through professional development in mathematics content, research-based teaching methods, and learning theory. Sufficient time and resources are needed for the selection process. Professional development specific to the instructional materials is needed for optimal use and often takes as long as three years for teachers to master. Finally, the process and the selections themselves should be evaluated to improve the next selection cycle.

Mathematics for All

Teaching

Assessment

Curriculum

Technology

Learning

Classroom Implications

Instructional materials that promote student learning in positive, innovative ways are selected because of their strong mathematical content, organization and structure, relationship to student experiences, teacher role, and assessment suggestions. However, high-quality instructional materials alone cannot ensure that learning will take place. Appropriate teacher use of instructional materials in classroom activities is vital to the effectiveness of the materials. Often, no one set of materials will be sufficient to meet classroom instructional needs, and teachers will want to use a variety of resources.

The mathematical content of the materials selected should reflect state or district mathematics standards. The organization of the program should include cohesive units, multi-day lessons, and worthwhile tasks that allow students sufficient time to explore and investigate in-depth mathematical ideas. Materials should develop understanding and abilities in mathematics and should clearly illustrate connections within mathematics and among other curriculum areas such as language arts, science, history, or art. Problem solving, communication, and reasoning should be built into the program at all levels.

Instructional materials should give students opportunities to be active learners, exploring and investigating mathematical ideas. Materials should ask students to communicate orally and in writing, both with one another and with the teacher. Technology and manipulatives should be used to explore mathematical ideas, model mathematical situations, analyze data, calculate numerical results, and solve problems.

Quality instructional materials provide suggestions to help students learn. The suggestions should elicit, engage, and challenge students' thinking, explain a variety of methods that give all students the opportunity to learn, and outline possible enriched or advanced work.

Student assessment should be integrated into the instructional program, using activities similar to learning activities. The materials should use multiple means of assessment and suggest ways to assess students individually or in small groups — through observations, oral and written work, student demonstrations or presentations, and student self-assessment. Conceptual understandings and procedural knowledge should be frequently assessed through tasks that ask students to apply mathematical knowledge in novel situations.

References

Association of State Supervisors of Mathematics, & National Council of Supervisors of Mathematics. (1993). Guide to selecting instructional materials for mathematics education.

Ball, D. L. (1997). Developing mathematics reform: What don't we know about teacher learning—but would make good working hypotheses.

Goldsmith, L. T., Mark, J., & Kantrov, I. (1998). Choosing a standards-based mathematics curriculum.

Muther, C. (1988). Textbook adoption: A process for decision making. A workshop manual.

National Council of Teachers of Mathematics. (1991). Position statement on selecting instructional materials.

National Research Council. (1999). Designing mathematics or science curriculum programs: A guide for using mathematics and science education standards.

Texas Statewide Systemic Initiative, Charles A. Dana Center, University of Texas at Austin (1998). Instructional materials analysis and selection for instructional materials implementation.

In what ways can integrating curriculum enhance learning in mathematics?

Interconnections among the disciplines . . . support learning by making the mathematics curriculum more meaningful.

Research and Best Practice

In real life, learning experiences are not separated into academic disciplines or subject areas. A student's classroom experiences should mirror this. Interconnections among the disciplines, when emphasized at all grade levels, will support learning by making the mathematics curriculum more meaningful.

Brain research has shown that long-term memory, or true learning, depends upon information that makes sense and has meaning. Subject integration helps a student make sense and understand the meaning of new information. Without these connections, students' learning experiences would add up to a collection of miscellaneous topics and unrelated facts. As early as 1938, John Dewey warned that isolation in all forms is to be avoided and we should strive for connectedness. *Benchmarks for Science Literacy* states that interconnected knowledge should be designed to "see the relationships among science, mathematics, and technology and between them and other human endeavors." (p. 320)

If the goal is to produce mathematically literate citizens who can apply mathematical thinking in real-life problem solving, then subject integration is essential. Problem-based learning, using real-life problems, serves as a powerful motivational tool. When connections are extended across curriculum areas, they establish a mental framework that can be recalled for future problem solving. This approach helps students see commonalities among diverse topics and reinforces understanding and meaning for future applications. Students can apply their newly gained knowledge to questions they have about why things happen in their world and discuss social implications.

The integration of subject areas often reveals an interdependency among the disciplines. For example, mathematics is used to calculate the number of calories from fat eaten in a week and find daily caloric averages in science. Integrating subject areas also increases the chances of stimulating student motivation by connecting to an area of interest. An example of this may be connecting physics with physical education or sports, mathematics with music, literature with history, or botany with fine arts.

Classroom Implications

There are many models for integrating curriculum in the classroom. Curriculum integration may be designed and implemented by an individual classroom teacher or created by a collaborative, team effort. Integrated or thematic units may be taught individually or by a multidisciplinary team of teachers, coordinating topics among otherwise separate departments. School culture often determines the most practical method for subject integration.

Mathematics can be effectively integrated at all grade levels with science, language arts, social studies, physical education, and fine arts, among other areas. Language arts (reading, writing, and communication) should be a strong component of all the disciplines. Mathematics and science are natural partners, sharing similar goals of building process and problem-solving skills. The integration of mathematics and science provides innovative projects that encourage students to learn. For example, asking students to build a weight-bearing bridge requires students to budget, do a cost analysis of their project, and conceptualize and communicate how their completed project will look before having built it.

There are many avenues of integration between mathematics and social studies. History often revolves around great advances in mathematics, and a study of important mathematical ideas helps students conceptualize the concepts of mathematics and see how ideas change over time. Both societal and mathematical perspectives can provide learning opportunities.

The challenges to subject integration are lack of imagination, inadequate teacher training, hindrances to teacher collaboration, and insufficient materials. However, the benefits to the learning process should spur teachers beyond those limitations to develop quality, integrated curricula.

References

American Association for the Advancement of Science, Project 2061. (1993). Benchmarks for science literacy.

Bailey, T. (1997). Integrating vocational and academic education.

Hoachlander, G. (1997). Organizing mathematics education around work.

Sousa, D. A. (1995). How the brain learns.

Westwater, A., & Wolfe, P. (2000). The brain-compatible curriculum.

Mathematics for All

Teaching

Assessment

Curriculum

Technology

Learning

How does integrated instruction in mathematics affect teaching and learning?

Real problems do not come neatly divided into mathematics strands.

Research and Best Practice

The Learning Principle of the NCTM *Principles and Standards for School Mathematics* (*PSSM*) urges that classrooms be places where students regularly "engage in tasks and experiences designed to deepen and connect their knowledge." (p. 21) Integrated content and instruction in mathematics facilitates the development of these connections.

When mathematics is taught in rich and realistic contexts, rather than on a purely abstract basis, more students are able to build deep understanding. Conclusions from cognitive science indicate that knowledge taught in multiple contexts better supports permanent, functional learning of concepts. Students provided rich, demanding problems that build on, rather than simply repeat, previous learning, grow in understanding. International studies indicate that teachers in successful classrooms orchestrate learning by providing problems where students are likely to be able to apply prior learning to approach new problems. Students who learn mathematics through complex problems and projects outperform other students whose learning is more compartmentalized and abstract in every area except facility in abstract symbol manipulation. Particularly, they are willing to apply all relevant previous learning to new problem situations, incorporating common sense and confidence with their mathematics skills in order to reach a solution.

Business and industry require workers who can think, solve problems and have integrated their knowledge. School experiences need to help build this integration. Real problems do not come neatly divided into mathematics strands. Often they require collecting real data (statistics and measurements), representing it visually (e.g., with coordinate geometry), then determining an equation that closely approximates the shape of the data (algebra) in order to predict future values for the situation (probability).

Through classrooms that provide rich problem situations as a vehicle for learning mathematics, students develop a flexible understanding of the discipline and learn to integrate content and process strands of mathematics, learning when, how, and why to use their knowledge to solve unfamiliar problems.

Classroom Implications

Integrating the various branches of mathematics not only makes sense, it also saves time. As more and more mathematics topics enter a particular grade level's curriculum, teachers often ask, "Where will I get the time to teach an additional topic?" The key may be to teach related topics together.

There are a variety of mathematics programs supporting integrated instruction currently available for all grade levels. Each uses challenging contextual problems to develop understanding of important mathematics. Mathematics programs from the past often have not helped students to make connections either within mathematics or with other subjects. At the elementary level, though text materials usually contain chapters on various mathematics strands, each is isolated from the others. Meanwhile, the conclusions of cognitive science indicate the importance of making connections in order to make transfer of learning possible.

Teachers new to integrated mathematics might begin to learn by using problems from these programs and observing the struggles and new learning of their students. They might also examine the growing number of achievement studies of students in integrated programs.

Some considerations regarding an integrated approach to mathematics instruction:

- Engagement does not guarantee learning. Students can be interested without learning new mathematics.
- Problem solving is not the same as solving word problems. Students need to struggle with a problem they do not yet know how to solve, but to which they can apply known mathematics. Allowing students to struggle enhances learning.
- True integration is not obvious by casual observation. An assortment of topics in a program may not indicate integration of content. Integration can only be determined when a teacher sees through teaching how ideas connect and are built upon.

One of the most important roles for a mathematics teacher is to select rich, integrated mathematical tasks and problems, ones that are accessible for all students, yet challenging enough for students at all levels of achievement to help each grow in mathematical understanding.

References

Boaler, J. (1997). Experiencing school mathematics: Teaching styles, sex, and setting.

Bransford, J. D., Brown, A. L., & Cocking, R. R. (Eds.) (1999). How people learn: Brain, mind, experience, and school.

Froelich, G. (1991). Connecting mathematics.

Hiebert, J., Carpenter, T. P., Fennema, E., Fuson, K. C., Wearne, D., Murray, H., Olivier, A., & Human, P. (1997) Making sense: Teaching and learning mathematics with understanding.

Hiebert, J. (1999) Relationship between research and the NCTM Standards.

National Council of Teachers of Mathematics. (2000) Principles and standards for school mathematics.

Stigler, J. W., & Hiebert, J. (1999) The teaching gap: Best ideas from the world's teachers for improving education in the classroom.

Thorson, A. (Ed.). (2000). Mathematics and science in the real world.

Mathematics For All

Teaching

Assessment

Curriculum

Technology

Learning

How does classroom curriculum connect to the outside world?

> **"We should all learn mathematics because it is useful, beautiful, and fun. . . . Teachers of mathematics are obliged, I believe, to do everything in their power to help their students experience the joy of mathematics."**
>
> Willoughby, S. S., 2000, p. 10-11.

Research and Best Practice

Children learn both inside and outside the classroom. It is a primary responsibility of the mathematics teacher to connect these two realms of knowledge and use those connections to augment understanding of both worlds. Real life is a rich source of mathematics problems. Learning is highly interactive as students explore problems, formulate ideas, and check those ideas with peers and with their teacher through discussion and collaboration. Students build new concepts as they recognize the connections between previous learning, intuition, formalized structures, mathematical strands, and other disciplines. Students create mathematical tools and aids — symbols, schemas, and visual models — during the learning process to move from concrete reality to more abstract higher-level thinking skills.

School mathematics has shifted from a fixed body of knowledge calling for the mechanistic manipulation of numbers, symbols, and geometric proofs, to mathematics as a human endeavor. Learning mathematics involves tasks that lead to discovering why techniques work, inventing new algorithms, and justifying solutions. Task selection criteria include:

- Do the tasks build on prior knowledge? Do they proceed from informal ideas to more formal understanding? Are they sequenced in increasing complexity? Do they connect to other mathematics domain strands and to other disciplines?

- Do the tasks lead to model construction, evaluation, and revision?

- Do the tasks lead to inquiry and justification? Is the student asked to make conjectures? to formulate a solution plan? to solve? to conclude? to justify that conclusion? Do the tasks lead students to self-question? to question others? to research? to evaluate and reevaluate?

- Are the tasks relevant to students? Is there intrinsic motivation in the tasks? Do they foster personal ownership? Do they allow for unique approaches based on an individual's own knowledge? Are the tasks challenging enough to be engaging, but not so challenging that they produce too much cognitive conflict?

Classroom Implications

Mathematics teachers need to know mathematics content, mathematics pedagogy, and how their students understand mathematical concepts. To design an appropriate curriculum, teachers need to know their students and their students' families, as well as their activities and interests. Teachers must be familiar with their students' mathematical strengths, misconceptions, favorite problem-solving approaches, and readiness to use mathematical tools. Since engaging mathematics capitalizes on realistic settings, the context of investigations is important. For instance, if students work problems that ask them to cut pizzas for fair sharing, the rational number concepts associated with such divisions will be more memorable.

Selecting problems for students to solve is one of the most important things a mathematics teacher does. The problems need to

- engage students' thinking
- focus on the development of conceptual understanding
- help students make connections and develop frameworks for ideas
- ask students to formulate questions and reason mathematically
- promote communication about mathematics
- portray mathematics as a "human endeavor"
- focus on diverse background experiences and dispositions
- develop all students' dispositions to do mathematics

If these problems connect to the real world outside the mathematics classroom, students will experience enhanced learning.

Following the publication of the *Curriculum and Evaluation Standards for School Mathematics* (1989), the National Science Foundation funded the development of standards-based curricula at all three grade band levels that were to reflect rich problem-solving contexts. These are now published, are used in many districts, and are helping students connect mathematical ideas and situations. Textbook companies are also developing materials to address the standards, including the design of curricula that connect students to the world outside the classroom.

References

Fennema, E., & Franke, M. L. (1992). Teachers' knowledge and its impact.

National Council of Teachers of Mathematics. (1989). Curriculum and evaluation standards for school mathematics.

National Council of Teachers of Mathematics. (1991). Professional teaching standards for school mathematics.

National Council of Teachers of Mathematics. (2000). Principles and standards for school mathematics.

Romberg, T., & Kaput, J. (1999). Mathematics worth teaching, mathematics worth understanding.

Siegler, R. (1998). Children's thinking.

Streefland, L. (1991). Fractions in realistic mathematics education: A paradigm of developing research.

Willoughby, S. S. (2000). Perspectives on mathematics education.

Mathematics For All

Teaching

Assessment

Curriculum

Technology

Learning

Instructional Technology
In Mathematics

Instructional technology refers to the tools used to promote classroom learning. In mathematics teaching, instructional technology is used in problem solving, thereby making the learning experience more learner-centered. Specific technologies include various types of calculators, handheld data-collection devices, computers, associated software, and the Internet.

Benefits of the use of instructional technology include increased accuracy and speed in data collection and graphing, real-time visualization, interactive modeling of invisible mathematical processes, ability to collect, compute, and analyze large volumes of data, collaboration for data collection and interpretation, and more varied presentations of results. Technology can make mathematics class more meaningful and standards more attainable for all students, and in particular for females and students with special needs. The Technology Principle from the National Council of Teachers of Mathematics (NCTM) *Principles and Standards for School Mathematics* (*PSSM*) states "technology should be used widely and responsibly, with the goal of enriching students' learning of mathematics." (pg. 25)

How can using instructional technology affect mathematics reasoning and problem solving?

Technology allows us to teach some traditional topics in a new way as well as teach new topics that are not accessible to our students without the technology.

Research and Best Practice

Mathematicians have always taken advantage of the technology available to them. Whether it be constructing a bisector of an angle with straightedge and compass or constructing a bridge using Computer Assisted Design, technology tools are an important part of a mathematics program. Today, both teachers and students should take advantage of video, CD-ROMs, calculators, computers, the Internet, and so on.

Technology allows us to teach some traditional topics in a new way as well as teach new topics that are not accessible to our students without the technology. Computer-Assisted Instruction (CAI) continues to expand. At first, drill-and-practice programs were shown to benefit students having difficulties with basic facts and algorithms. However, today's CAI programs include complex problem-solving software that permits students to address problems in individual ways. Students can try things out, see the consequences, and then refine their thinking if unsuccessful. In this way, they are able to construct their own knowledge.

Calculators permit students to check their work or attack a problem using a different approach. Certain fraction calculators permit students to choose a common factor to reduce improper fractions to simplest form. The calculator doesn't stand in judgment. It merely accepts and uses students' suggestions or rejects them and allows the students to try again. Looking at where a quadratic function crosses the x-axis using a graphing calculator is another way to solve a quadratic equation. It allows the student to see the connection between algebra and analytic geometry.

Sensor probes can be used with the computer or graphing calculators to obtain real-time data. The Internet permits students to obtain real data from all over the world. Employing such sets of data makes the mathematics used come alive. Students using such technologies are likely to show greater persistence and effectiveness in trying to solve problems and are more apt to take risks.

Classroom Implications

Two concerns must be addressed when using technology. Whether or not to use technology in the first place must be addressed. Students still need to know the basic facts and most of the algorithms used in a traditional mathematics program. Technologies can assist and support those aspects of the program but should not replace them. The NCTM Technology Principle emphasizes that tools allow students to focus on decision making, reflection, reasoning, and problem solving, without being used as a replacement for basic understanding.

Additionally, teachers must assure equity within their school. These technologies are not just for the remedial or the advanced student. They should be made available to all students. When used properly, technology motivates students to become more interested in mathematics. A student can conjecture and explore possible solutions to problems. Some of these tools permit students with limited physical abilities to participate as equals.

As new forms of technology are developed and become available to schools, teachers need to become flexible and creative with their use. Often, technological devices permit students to work more on their own, with the teacher as a guide or fellow problem-solver rather than as a presenter. Understandably, there will be forthcoming innovations that will permit the teacher to present concepts in new and exciting ways.

Teachers must be willing to take the time and effort to learn these new approaches, independently or through staff development programs. Only when the teacher knows the many potential uses of technological instructional devices can he or she properly assess their utility in a mathematics program.

References

Australian Association of Mathematics Teachers (AAMT). (1996). Statement on the use of technology for mathematics in Australian schools.

Cradler, J. (n.d.). Summary of current research and evaluation findings on technology in education.

Leadership and the New Technologies. (1999, March/April). News briefs. 1999 Research report on the effectiveness of technology in schools.

Wellburn, E. (1996, May). The status of technology in the education system: A literature review.

What effect do calculators have on student learning?

Teachers using calculators for instruction can employ these technological strengths, such as speed, to enhance student learning.

Research and Best Practice

Calculator technology can be used in various ways in mathematics classrooms beyond replacing paper-and-pencil computation. Potential uses include developing number sense, exploring mathematical concepts such as geometry, representing and graphing data, and solving complex problems. Resistance to the use of calculators in the teaching and learning of mathematics has been voiced. However, the calculator-use research concludes that when calculators were used in a variety of ways, students performed as well as, or better than, those who used paper-and-pencil methods. Internationally, as students' in-class calculator use increased, so did their level of performance on mathematics assessments.

Students using calculators

- Have higher math achievement than non-calculator users even when they can choose any tool desired
- Do better on mental computation than non-calculator users
- Experience more varied concepts and computations
- Have improved attitudes toward mathematics
- Do not become overly reliant on calculators

Graphing calculators can reduce the need to manipulate algebraic expressions or equations, yet studies show that students who learn in a technological environment with a related algebra curriculum perform better on standard algebra manipulations as well as modeling and problem solving.

Computing technologies enhance both the teaching and learning of mathematics. For benefits to occur, the technology's power needs to be used to enable student exploration and to promote generalizations. Studies indicate that such things as gender differences disappear on student performance when students use graphing calculators.

Classroom Implications

Teachers using calculators for instruction can employ these technological tools for their strengths, such as speed, to enhance student learning. Students can work multiple problems or solve more difficult ones using a calculator in the same amount of time as was spent using the paper-and-pencil method. This time gain allows students to try different approaches to problem solving. Calculators allow students to move at their own pace and concentrate on the mathematics of problem solving rather than the arithmetic to be computed. Students who do not have full computational competencies can solve problems that are intellectually challenging.

Inquiry learning can be enhanced through the use of a graphing calculator. Graphing calculators prompt more student discussions. The teacher can become the facilitator in the classroom while the students investigate the mathematical concepts, such as slope of a line or matrix multiplication.

Studies show that mathematical problem solving is enhanced by the use of calculators because students

- Feel more confident in initiating problem solving
- Do more exploration
- Focus more on the problem to be solved and less on the algorithm for solving it
- Explain their strategies through deductive reasoning more consistently and interpret answers more readily
- Are more successful if weak in basic facts

Students need to learn the capabilities of the various technologies, including calculators. Knowing what each tool can do allows students to determine which tool to select for which purpose — and whether or not to use a tool at all.

References

Demana, F., & Waits, B. (1990). Enhancing mathematics teaching and learning through technology.

Groves, S., & Stacey, K. (1998). Calculators in primary mathematics: Exploring number before teaching algorithms.

Kelley, M. (1985). The effect of the use of the hand-held calculator on the development of problem-solving strategies.

Leinhardt, G., Zaslavsky, O., & Stein, M. K. (1990). Functions, graphs, and graphing: Tasks, learning, and teaching.

Moschkovich, J., & Schoenfeld, A. H. (1993). Aspects of understanding: On multiple perspectives and representation of linear relations and connections among them.

Shumway, R., White, A., Wheatley, G., Reys, R., Coburn, T., & Schoen, H. (1981, March). Initial effects of calculators in elementary school mathematics.

Wheatley, C. (1980). Calculator use and problem-solving performance.

How can technology make mathematics teaching more learner-centered?

> *"If you use graphing calculators, you arouse their interest. Students do not open a math book and say, 'Let me show you what I know on this page,' but they will show you what they know about a single button on a graphing calculator."*
>
> Moses, R. P., & Cobb, C. E., Jr., 2001, p.117.

Research and Best Practice

Instructional technology empowers students by improving their skills and concepts through multiple representations; enhanced visualization; increased construction of mathematics meaning; and individualized and customized diagnoses, remediation, and evaluation. Instructional technology facilitates

- visualization of mathematical ideas
- organization and analysis of data
- computational efficiency and accuracy

It frees students to conjecture, solve problems, analyze, synthesize, and evaluate. From external symbol systems and structured learning environments to internal personal constructs, imagery, and heuristics, technology aids in representating and communicating mathematics.

Technology allows students more autonomy in practicing higher-order thinking skills. Increasing access to primary resources and large data sets opens opportunities for students to select learning contexts and design investigations. Real-world problems make learning mathematics more exciting for students. Instructional technology creates an active environment in which students can communicate with working mathematicians and gather data in various environments. They not only solve problems, but also define problems of interest to themselves and receive instantaneous feedback on the accuracy of their ideas.

Many instructional technologies are tools for problem solving. Calculators, spreadsheets, graphing programs, function probes, "mathematical supposers" for making and checking conjectures, and programs modeling complex phenomena provide cognitive scaffolds to promote complex thinking, design, and learning. Such activities are motivating often because they are learner-focused and authentic; they encourage critical thinking, and they create lasting knowledge.

Instructional technology broadens the learning community. When students collaborate, they share the process of constructing ideas. This encourages learners to reflect on their ideas in ways generally not seen in classroom instruction. Current interests can be productively pursued; timeframes do not hinder; intellectual barriers can be broken down; and creativity, individuality, and desire to learn can be maximized.

Classroom Implications

When student mathematics experiences are integrated with technology, the classroom becomes more student-centered. The teacher, as a facilitator, moves throughout the classroom, assisting individual children or the group as a whole. The teacher's role in using instructional technology is to help students internalize concepts that can be derived from symbols, graphs, or other technological representations of mathematics.

The use of instructional technology in learning mathematics allows students to use a variety of design strategies such as problem solving, creative and critical thinking, visual imagery, and reasoning; hands-on abilities such as measuring, drawing and sketching, working with computers, and using tools; and quality control mechanisms such as appropriate assessment and evaluative techniques. When students design their own learning environments, they can become skilled in the use and maintenance of technological products and systems, and they can assess the appropriateness of these tools and systems.

It is not the equipment in the classroom, but how the equipment is used that makes the difference in student understanding. For example, tools such as dynamic geometry software allow students to construct mathematical knowledge rather than memorize facts and formulas. The key to success lies in finding the appropriate points for integrating technology into mathematics, so that it supports the understanding and reflection students must do.

References

Bransford, J. D., Brown, A. L., & Cocking, R. R. (Eds.). (1999). How people learn: Brain, mind, experience, and school.

Burke, M. J., & Curcio, F. R. (Eds.). (2000). Learning mathematics for a new century. 2000 yearbook.

Cuoco, A. A. (Ed.). (2001). The roles of representation in school mathematics. 2001 yearbook.

International Society for Technology in Education. (2000). National educational technology standards for students: Connecting curriculum and technology.

International Technology Education Association. (2000). Standards for technological literacy: Content for the study of technology.

Kimmins, D., & Bouldin, E. (1996, March). Teaching the prospective teacher: Making mathematics come alive with technology.

Moses, R. P., & Cobb, C. E., Jr. (2001). Radical equations: math literacy and civil rights.

Wenglinsky, H. (1998). Does it compute? The relationship between educational technology and student achievement in mathematics.

Mathematics For All

Teaching

Assessment

Curriculum

Technology

Learning

How can students best use information and data from the Internet?

Using current real-world data provides mathematics teachers and students with an enriching resource that cannot be duplicated in a textbook.

Research and Best Practice

The *PSSM* Technology Principle emphasizes that instructional technology tools allow students to focus on decision making, reflection, reasoning, and problem solving, and to enhance basic understanding. One such tool, available in many classrooms, is the Internet.

The Internet provides a wealth of information from around the world. In addition, it can provide information on events almost as they happen. Realizing that this information is only as good as its source, and that there are no filters on what might be posted on Web sites, teachers and students need to focus on evaluating and selecting reputable, usable information.

Using current real-world data provides mathematics teachers and students with an enriching resource that cannot be duplicated in a textbook. Working on a problem that is in the news sparks student interest and may relate to what is being studied in other classes. Real data answers the question, "What is this good for?" Population figures, acid rain amounts, or the latest medical breakthroughs are data that can be used in mathematics classroom activities.

Real-world data tends to be messier than data sets supplied in textbooks; no longer does the data set for a particular problem have to result in integral solutions. The use of computer software and sophisticated calculators can give the student access to methods for solving problems using this complicated real data. Students can use the technology available to them to conjecture, simulate situations, and refine their answers. Technology permits the students to ask and try to answer their own questions generated by the data.

Classroom Implications

Students live in the information age. They read and hear of happenings around the world that interest them. Teachers can take advantage of this interest by using data from the Internet to provide the context for mathematics lessons in the classroom.

Looking at population growth patterns in various states or countries, students can graph the data and make predictions about the size of future generations. Middle-level students might estimate the slopes of lines or curves and discuss interpretations, while high school students might use their technologies to find regression lines of best fit.

In addition to taking data from Web sites, students might be able to communicate about data and related mathematical procedures with other mathematics students from around the nation or the world. Students can exchange data and perhaps share data, calculations, interpretations, and reports on a variety of topics such as weather or voter preferences.

The ability of the student to communicate mathematics effectively with another person outside of the classroom is a highly desired skill. Presenting data and the conclusions reached from that data does not come easily, so instruction that emphasizes these skills should be part of a K–12 mathematics curriculum.

Teachers will need to carefully screen Internet sites before student use, evaluate the credibility of the sources, and determine the usefulness of the data. Some sites contain data sets that may be too extensive, too complex, or in an inaccessible format for the intended instructional purpose. While evaluation of sources is initially a teacher responsibility, one focus of ongoing student instruction that utilizes Internet resources needs to be how to perform this type of evaluation.

References

Beck, S. (2000). The good, the bad and the ugly or why it's a good idea to evaluate web sources?

Frand, J. L. (2000). The information-age mindset.

International Society for Technology in Education. (2000). National educational technology standards for students: Connecting curriculum and technology.

Land, S. M., & Greene, B. A. (2000). Project-based learning with the World Wide Web: A qualitative study of resource integration.

Roempler, K. S. (1999). Using the Internet in the classroom: Becoming a critical consumer of the web.

Wenglinsky, H. (1998). Does it compute? The relationship between educational technology and student achievement in mathematics.

Mathematics For All

Teaching

Assessment

Curriculum

Technology

Learning

How has technology changed the mathematics that is important for students to learn?

Mathematics students will have access to fields of mathematics previously reserved for experts.

Research and Best Practice

Most mathematics teachers understand that the use of classroom technology strongly affects how mathematics is taught. Its appropriate use also influences the content and order of the mathematics curriculum. Some topics already included in the curriculum become more important because effective use of technology requires their understanding. These include number sense, rounding, establishment of range and domain, and communication through spreadsheets. Other topics traditionally included in the mathematics curriculum become less important because the use of calculator and computer technology replaces them. These topics include multidigit computation, complicated factoring, and hand-drawing of complex graphs. It is possible to include some new mathematics content because modern technology allows access to it. This new content includes several topics which relate to the world of work, including working with large matrices, continuous compounding of interest, and creation and interpretation of fractals.

Through the use of instructional technologies, students and teachers are better able to

  • Engage in meaningful and challenging mathematics tasks
  • Interact with mathematical ideas in innovative ways that allow active student participation
  • Build knowledge that reflects different models of instruction and different approaches to the learning of mathematics

Instructional technology, such as calculators, dynamic software, and computer simulations, permits investigation of the relationships within and between mathematical topics. Students make connections among various mathematical ideas while exploring relationships efficiently by using graphical displays and computer simulations.

Achievement in higher-order thinking skills is positively related to the use of technology. Calculators and other technologies help students focus clearly on mathematical concepts. These technologies allow students to observe mathematically accurate patterns and to form conjectures. Problem-solving techniques are strengthened, and deductive reasoning is enhanced because students can seek answers to their own "what-if" questions.

Classroom Implications

The use of instructional technologies in the mathematics classroom not only increases the types of content that can be taught, it also may decrease the utility of some traditional content. Decisions about what is or is not obsolete mathematics content must be made thoughtfully, recognizing not just what technology can do, but analyzing carefully what students need to be able to do and how they need to be able to reason. The curriculum must still be about the mathematics, not about the technology. The most important instructional decision is how the technology fits with the purpose of the lesson.

The choice of problems posed in the mathematics classroom is critical to instructional success. With technology, the pool of problems from which to choose and the ways they can be presented changes.

Mathematics teachers incorporating technology into the curriculum need to

- Create a vision for the appropriate use of technology in the mathematics classroom
- Choose technologies to further established learning goals
- Determine whether the role of the selected technology is to replace a capacity that the student might otherwise need to develop or to develop the student's capacity to think independently of the technology
- Provide resources to help students gain power and fluency with the technological tools
- Adapt technology for individual student needs

A developmental approach to technology use chooses a limited number of tools, introduces them early, and uses them consistently. Such an approach develops increased skill and sophistication in using the technology, as well as mathematical skills, to enhance student achievement. How much and how well students are learning to think mathematically parallels the effective use of technology for the purposes described here.

Through this kind of teacher planning, mathematics students will have access to fields of mathematics previously reserved for experts. They will employ statisitics with large, realistic data sets and will learn real-world applications of discrete mathematics.

References

Brown, J., Collins, A., & Duguid, P. (1989). Situated cognition and the culture of learning.

Clements, D. H., & McMillen, S. (1996). Rethinking concrete manipulatives.

Groves, S., & Stacey, K. (1998). Calculators in primary mathematics: Exploring number before teaching algorithms.

Hembree, R., & Dessart, D. (1986). Effects of hand held calculators in pre-college mathematics education: A meta-analysis.

National Council of Supervisors of Mathematics. (1997). Supporting improvement in mathematics education: A public relations sourcebook.

Wenglinsky, H. (1998). Does it compute? The relationship between educational technology and student achievement in mathematics.

Mathematics For All

Teaching

Assessment

Curriculum

Technology

Learning

Learning Mathematics

What does it mean to learn mathematics? This question is addressed in the National Council of Teachers of Mathematics (NCTM) *Principles and Standards for School Mathematics* (*PSSM*) . Children are natural learners. They are inquisitive about patterns and shapes, recognizing and creating them from a young age. They count, measure, and share objects. For children, mathematics is learned by doing. Their school experience of mathematics learning should include problem solving and reasoning through grade 12, not simply lectures, books, and worksheets.

During the twentieth century, educators' understanding of the learning process has progressed from behavioral observations through cognitive psychology into improved knowledge about neurophysiology. The 1990s were dubbed "the decade of the brain" because of the tremendous increase in understanding of how the brain works. Twenty-first century educators will improve their classroom practice through application of the newest understandings from neuroscience.

How can we communicate with the public about the importance of learning mathematics?

"In our technically oriented society, 'innumeracy' has replaced illiteracy as our principal educational gap.... [W]e live in an age of mathematics — the culture has been 'mathematized'."

National Academy of Sciences, 1996.

Research and Best Practice

The general public has become more aware and interested in mathematics education reform in the past 25 years. Publications such as the National Commission on Excellence in Education's *A Nation at Risk*, the standards-setting work of the National Council of Teachers of Mathematics and associated media publicity, and press coverage of reports from the Third International Mathematics and Science Study (TIMSS) have brought the reforms needed in education into the limelight. This public interest presents both an opportunity and an obligation for mathematics educators at all levels.

The value of learning mathematics in today's world may be addressed in the context of mathematical literacy for all students. Even though definitions may differ somewhat, most would agree that mathematical literacy encompasses not only knowledge of mathematics concepts and procedures but also the ability to apply that knowledge to create mathematical models of situations, solve the problem represented by the model, and interpret the solution in terms of the societal implications. The Glenn Commission Report, *Before It's Too Late*, cites four compelling reasons why students should become competent in mathematics and science: the pace of change in the global economy and the American workplace; the need for both mathematics and science in everyday decision-making; national security interests; and the intrinsic value of mathematics and science to our society.

The NCTM standards, *Principles and Standards for School Mathematics (PSSM`)*, and other state, local, and national documents define what all students need to know and be able to do in today's world and in the future. Such documents provide the specifications and framework for mathematical literacy. *PSSM* describes the vision, foundation, and goals for school mathematics. The vision is a future in which all students have access to rigorous, high-quality mathematics instruction, and all students value mathematics and engage actively in learning it. The Principles (equity, curriculum, teaching, learning, assessment, and technology) and the Standards (number and operations, algebra, geometry, measurement, data analysis and probability, problem solving, reasoning and proof, communications, connections, and representation) call for a common foundation of mathematics to be learned by all students. The goal of mathematics education is to help all students use mathematics to improve their own lives, become aware of their responsibilities as citizens, and prepare for a future of great and continual change.

Mathematics
Learning •

Mathematics For All

Teaching

Assessment

Curriculum

Technology

Learning

Classroom Implications

Mathematical literacy is the goal for all students, not just for those preparing for college or for a career dependent on higher-level mathematics. In a society heavily dependent on mathematics, mathematical literacy includes using mathematics-related knowledge on a personal and societal level, addressing issues by asking questions, using evidence to propose explanations or answers for those questions, and becoming informed citizens in a democratic society. Mathematics learning expectations must be high for all students. To promote the goal of mathematics literacy and the vision of quality mathematics education, the entire K–12 educational system must be aligned and focused on providing

- Important content in solid mathematics curricula
- Competent and knowledgeable mathematics teachers who can integrate instruction and assessment
- Education policies that support and enhance learning
- Connections across disciplines
- Mathematics classrooms with access to technology
- Preparation for future careers
- Tools and strategies to assist with making decisions on mathematics-based issues

Alignment of the K–12 educational system needs to include equity, curriculum, teaching, learning, assessment, and technology, the six Principles suggested in *PSSM*. To offer high quality, K–12 mathematics learning experiences for all students, there must be a consistent and coherent program taught by content-qualified teachers. Ongoing professional development opportunities provide teachers with learning experiences needed to teach mathematics effectively. Administrators need to offer positive support, such as providing access to mathematics resources; ensuring that a qualified, highly competent mathematics teacher is in every classroom; and promoting ongoing opportunities for professional development.

Outreach by mathematics educators to parents and the school community will achieve a shared commitment to improve mathematics education. Because parent attitudes about mathematics predict student success in mathematics classes, parents must help teachers guide students to an understanding of their critical need to learn mathematics.

References

Campbell, P. (1992). Math, science, and your daughter: What can parents do? Encouraging girls in math and science series.

Hyde, A. (2001, December). Another myth about math.

Leinwand, S. (1995, June 4). It's time to abandon computational drudgery, but not the computation.

National Academy of Sciences. (1996). Renewing U.S. mathematics.

National Commission on Mathematics and Science Teaching for the 21st Century. (2000). Before it's too late: A report to the nation from the National Commission on Mathematics and Science Teaching for the 21st Century.

National Council of Supervisors of Mathematics. (1997). Supporting improvement in mathematics education: A public relations sourcebook.

National Council of Teachers of Mathematics. (2000). Principles and standards for school mathematics.

National Research Council. (1989). Everybody counts: A report to the nation on the future of mathematics education.

What do we know about how students learn mathematics?

Students must have ample opportunities to learn, if they are to fully develop their mathematical proficiency.

Research and Best Practice

In the past decade, educators have greatly improved their understanding of how students learn mathematics. The use of manipulatives, a focus on algebraic concepts throughout the mathematics program, problems set in meaningful contexts, and ample opportunities and time to learn are important in studying mathematics. Research indicates that manipulatives can be effective in mathematics instruction when used properly. While primary teachers generally accept the importance of manipulatives, recent studies of students' mathematics learning have created interest in the use of manipulatives across all grades.

It is important, however, to keep the focus on mathematics, as students may learn only about the manipulative and miss the mathematics. Although manipulatives are particularly useful in helping students move from the concrete to the abstract level, teachers must carefully choose activities and manipulatives to effectively support the introduction of abstract symbols.

Students may have difficulty making the transition from arithmetic to algebra. Research indicates how the development of algebraic reasoning can be supported in elementary and middle school. Young students can learn algebra concepts, especially algebraic representation and the notion of variable and function, and basic concepts can be introduced as patterning and as a generalization of arithmetic. For example, patterns on a hundreds chart can be discovered and analyzed.

Students can learn best about mathematical topics through solving meaningful, contextual problems. Students can benefit somewhat from seeing problems solved, but they receive the most benefit from solving problems themselves. Appropriate questioning techniques by both teacher and student enhance the development of student problem-solving skills.

Students must have ample opportunities to learn, if they are to fully develop their mathematical proficiency. Students need school time for regular, sustained engagement in the study of mathematics, including meaningful practice built on understanding. Student practice is enhanced with timely feedback on work.

Mathematics For All

Teaching

Assessment

Curriculum

Technology

Learning

Classroom Implications

School programs should provide students rich activities involving number and operations that enable students to build on their informal learning or to learn without prior instruction. Students need to have experiences with concrete materials when learning concepts at any level, and instructional materials and classroom teaching should help students make the transition from the concrete to the abstract. Transition efforts are necessary to move from use of manipulatives to the abstract and a focus on the mathematics represented through the instructional materials is imperative.

Students must have a thorough understanding of the base-ten and decimal place-value number representations, and need to gain fluency with multidigit numbers and with decimal fractions. Students should experience learning activities from early elementary grades regarding algebraic concepts. Algebraic ideas should be developed in a fairly robust way in middle school and integrated with other mathematical concepts. Similarly, teachers could explore ways to introduce the central ideas of calculus, such as rate of change, to students throughout elementary and high school grades.

The mathematics classroom should provide rich opportunities for students to solve contextual problems. Problem-solving work should involve group activities as well as individual efforts, and students should have opportunities to verbalize their thought processes and interact with other students in collaborative work. Significant class time should be spent developing mathematical ideas and methods. Teacher questioning techniques should elicit students' thought processes and solution strategies and give students opportunities to develop greater clarity and precision. Classroom discourse should include discussion of mathematical connections, other solution methods, and mathematical justifications. Often, changing the form of a question from single-answer to one that allows students various ways to achieve an end result will increase student creativity and motivation. For example, beyond asking students to answer items like, "Simplify $4x + 3x$," students also could be asked questions like, "What are four ways to represent the function $y = 7x$?" The latter question assesses student understanding while stimulating more creative thought.

References

DeCorte, E., Greer, B., & Verschaffel, L. (1996). Mathematics teaching and learning.

Hiebert, J., & Carpenter, T. (1992). Learning and teaching with understanding.

Kilpatrick, J., Swafford, J., & Findell, B. (Eds.). (2001). Adding it up: Helping children learn mathematics.

Stroup, W. (1999, April). The structure of generative activity in group settings.

What does learning theory show teachers about how students learn mathematics?

> *"Students must learn mathematics with understanding, actively building new knowledge from experience and prior knowledge."*
>
> National Council of Teachers of Mathematics, 2000, p. 20.

Research and Best Practice

Knowledge changes throughout a person's development and is culturally and socially mediated. Students are not empty vessels to be filled with knowledge; rather, they build their own knowledge structures. The NCTM *Principles and Standards for School Mathematics* builds a case through its Learning Principle for going beyond rote memorization. "Students must learn mathematics with understanding, actively building new knowledge from experience and prior knowledge." (p. 20) Planning courses of action, weighing alternatives, applying prior knowledge to new ways of thinking or new ideas, and making sense of the world are instructional strategies supported by learning theory, as well as skills of informed citizenship.

The human brain is naturally curious, searching for patterns in sensory input and memory. It analyzes complex information into component parts, and synthesizes simple facts into concepts. The brain initially pays primary attention to the emotional content of information, but is capable of being focused through metacognition. Because it is changed by every act of learning, whether intentional or peripheral, each brain is unique. To make appropriate use of brain research on learning, mathematics teachers should link new instruction to students' prior knowledge by employing teaching strategies that draw on varied learning styles.

Teachers' use of learning theory encourages student-centered design of learning environments. Aligning instruction about facts, procedures, and concepts strengthens learning all three. New learning connects to material previously learned, thus becoming useful in powerful ways. This approach to teaching new material makes subsequent learning easier and encourages a sense of mathematical power.

A learning theory-based instructional approach offers students an opportunity to take control of their learning of mathematics through a more personal connection, which gives greater meaning to the acquired knowledge or skill. A mathematics classroom organized to promote learning, values and encourages student interaction and cooperation, provides access to learning materials from realistic contexts, and allows students to generate their own ways of learning.

Classroom Implications

Learning is not a passive activity. This belief provides a focus for educators to use learning theory in designing mathematics classrooms.

Sometimes students have misconceptions about mathematics topics, which should be corrected. Long-held concepts should be evaluated in light of new information, a complex and time-consuming process. Some misconceptions appear to be more tenacious than others. Thus effective teaching requires not only sound knowledge of correct mathematics information, but also knowledge of common misconceptions and how to deal with them. Without the latter, students' attempts to combine new instruction with prior misconceptions may have unanticipated learning outcomes.

Effective mathematics teachers play a pivotal role in helping students search for deeper knowledge and skill. They probe for greater justification of student-generated ideas and deeper explanations of relationships and of how mathematics works using questions such as

- How does this operation work?
- What generalization can you make from this mathematical situation? Defend your ideas.
- What alternative strategy can you develop for this procedure?
- How can you justify your answer?
- What patterns or relationships apply to this problem? Describe the ones you found.

These types of questions emphasize student-to-student interactions and justification of their ideas, while valuing their knowledge and skill. The teacher, therefore, does not dominate the material or the conversation. Instead, the teacher's role is to help students shape their ideas while simultaneously honing their skills.

Students of teachers who plan instruction based on learning theory are more likely to take intellectual risks. They are willing to accept challenges to their misconceptions. Students building new learning demonstrate their understanding rather than repeating what they are taught. Teachers who model building mathematical knowledge and who design learning environments that support it are honoring their students as emerging mathematicians.

References

Bransford, J. D., Brown, A. L., & Cocking, R. R. (Eds.). (1999). How people learn: Brain, mind, experience, and school.

Brooks, J. G., & Brooks, M. G. (1993). In search of understanding: The case for constructivist classrooms.

Caine, R. N., & Caine, G. (1994). Making connections: Teaching and the human brain.

Duckworth, E. (1987). The having of wonderful ideas and other essays on teaching and learning.

National Council of Teachers of Mathematics. (2000). Principles and standards for school mathematics.

Nunley, K. F. (1999). The regular educator's guide to the brain.

Resnick, L. B., & Klopfer, L. E., (1989). Toward the thinking curriculum: Current cognitive research.

Steffe, L. P., & Wiegel, H. G. (1996). On the nature of a model of mathematical learning.

Tsuruda, G. (1994). Putting it together: Middle school math in transition.

Mathematics for All

Teaching

Assessment

Curriculum

Technology

Learning

What is the role of basic skills in mathematics instruction?

> "The automaticity in putting a skill to use frees up mental energy to focus on the more rigorous demands of a complicated problem."
>
> Wu, H., 1999, p. 15.

Research and Best Practice

An early definition of basic mathematical skills, perhaps before the advent of the national standards or even before the 1980 NCTM *Agenda for Action*, referred only to computation, arithmetic facts, and symbol manipulation. Today, it is clearly important that students solve problems, apply mathematics in everyday situations, use logical reasoning, and have an understanding of basic concepts of algebra, geometry, measurement, statistics or data analysis, and probability. All of these topics are incorporated in the new definition of basic mathematics skills.

Many of these topics that form the new definition of basic skills are discussed in other articles in this volume, so here we focus only on arithmetic. For example, command of addition, subtraction, multiplication, and division facts are essential in understanding computational processes. Students who commit basic facts to memory and become computationally fluent spend more time on the problem-solving process and thereby are more likely to become successful problem solvers. Automatic access to basic facts frees up a student's mental processes to allow directed focus on problem solving.

It is also important to note that there is abundant research evidence that proficient calculation skills and basic facts mastery need not precede conceptual understanding and problem solving. Students find well-chosen problems that are motivating and interesting to be an aid in learning and retaining mathematical ideas. Even basic facts can be learned relatively effortlessly through meaningful repetition in the context of solving problems or playing games. When students encounter a variety of contexts and tasks, they have more opportunity to develop and use thinking strategies that support and reinforce learning facts.

As mathematics teachers make increasing use of emerging calculator and computer technologies, enhanced conceptions of basic skills in arithmetic and algebra are appearing. Greater emphasis will be placed on number sense/symbol sense and strategies for mental computation and reasoned estimation. Diminished attention can be paid to paper-and-pencil routines for complex calculation as mathematics students use the power of technology.

Classroom Implications

Students trying to master the basic arithmetic facts should be given efficient strategies. For example, 7 + 8 can be thought of as (7 + 7) + 1, and the answer to 7 x 8 can be determined from (5 x 8) + (2 x 8), or from (7 x 7) + 7. Such strategies are built on number sense and meaningful mathematical relationships. These relationships make it easier for students to learn new facts because they are generating new knowledge rather than relying strictly on memorization. Derived fact strategies improve recall and provide fall-back mechanisms for students. Facts and methods learned with understanding are connected; they are easier to remember and use, and they can be reconstructed when forgotten. Learning with understanding is more powerful than simply memorizing because the act of organizing improves retention, promotes fluency, and facilitates learning related material.

Measurement basic skills learned at the elementary level can be useful to students learning formal algebraic basic skills in high school. The product of the multiplication of two binomials (x + 2) and (x + 3) can be thought of as the area of a rectangle having sides with lengths (x + 2) and (x + 3). The result is one "big" square (x by x), five rectangles (1 by x), and 6 "little" squares (1 by 1), or $x^2 + 5x + 6$.

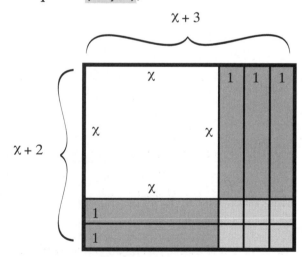

Procedural knowledge should be developed on a foundation of conceptual understanding. Practice toward mastery should not precede meaning. Drill does not guarantee immediate recall and does not contribute to growth in understanding. Practice is important, but practice without understanding may be destructive. Once students understand a computation procedure, practice will help them become confident and competent in using it. But when students mimic a procedure without understanding, it is difficult for them to go back later and build understanding.

References

Charles, R., & Lobato, J. (1998). Future basics: Developing mathematical power.

Fuson, K. C. (1992). Research on learning and teaching addition and subtraction of whole numbers.

Hiebert, J., & Carpenter, T. P. (1992). Learning and teaching with understanding.

Kilpatrick, J., Swafford, J., & Findell, B. (Eds.). (2001). Adding it up: Helping children learn mathematics.

National Council of Teachers of Mathematics. (1980). An agenda for action: Recommendations for school mathematics of the 1980s.

National Council of Teachers of Mathematics. (2000). Principles and standards for school mathematics.

Wu, H. (1999, Fall). Basic skills versus conceptual understanding: A bogus dichotomy in mathematics education.

Mathematics For All

Teaching

Assessment

Curriculum

Technology

Learning

What is the role of algorithms in mathematics instruction?

> "[R]ather than stressing the mastery of specific algorithms — which are now carried out principally by calculators or computers — school mathematics can instead emphasize more fundamental attributes of algorithms (e.g., speed, efficiency, sensitivity) that are essential for intelligent use of mathematics in a computer age. Learning to think algorithmically builds contemporary mathematical literacy."
>
> Steen, L. A., 1990, p. 7.

Research and Best Practice

Algorithms and algorithmic study are important mathematical ideas that all students need to understand and use. An algorithm is a precise, step-by-step method or set of rules for solving problems of a particular type. Algorithmic study involves applying, developing, analyzing, and understanding the nature of algorithms. Although there are algorithms of many types and in all fields of mathematics, this article focuses on algorithms associated with arithmetic operations.

Questions about the emphasis on and teaching of well established (standard or conventional) arithmetic algorithms are the subject of debate, especially between traditional and reform approaches. Research foci in recent studies about algorithmic development and computational fluency include: the value of standard, student-invented, and alternative algorithms; the value and place of drill in learning algorithms; and the place of algorithms in a technological world.

In order to become fluent in calculation, students must have efficient, accurate methods supported by number and operation sense. They must learn how algorithms work. Thoughtful use of standard algorithms advances fluency. However, rote learning of these traditional paper-and-pencil algorithms can interfere with the development of number sense. Alternative or student-invented algorithms are often more successful, especially when they build on student thinking about the operations.

Practice plays an important role in teaching and learning mathematics at all levels; however, it can be appropriate or inappropriate. Drill and practice is inappropriate when it involves an incorrect procedure or a method that makes no sense to the student. If practice occurs too soon (without conceptual understanding or prior to experiences with other methods), it is difficult for students to focus on meaning. Further, early introduction and practice of algorithms may legitimize a single procedure and limit students' computational fluency so that they cannot choose methods that best fit the numbers or situation.

Speed and efficiency in using arithmetic algorithms with large numbers is not as critical as it once was. There is little value in drilling to achieve such a goal. But many everyday mathematics tasks require facility with algorithms for computation. Technology has not made obsolete the need to understand and be able to perform some basic written algorithms.

Classroom Implications

Mathematics teachers making decisions about using algorithms in specific lessons must keep in mind the three research foci identified previously. Learning to use "standard" algorithms should be part of the mathematics curriculum. In addition to providing computational tools, algorithms can be important tools in their own right. They can be analyzed and compared, helping students understand the nature and properties of operations, place-value concepts for numbers, and characteristics of good algorithms.

Mathematics teachers need to understand the importance of alternative algorithms invented by students. Providing opportunities for students to develop and discuss invented algorithms helps to enhance number and operation sense. When students are engaged in development of computational methods or in recording, explaining, and critiquing one another's strategies, they can learn about efficiency, validity, and generalizability. In lessons focused on the development and discussion of strategies, various standard algorithms may arise naturally, or they can be introduced by the teacher as appropriate.

Appropriate practice is connected to mathematical thinking through reasoning, communicating, and problem solving. Appropriate practice reminds students that mathematics is well-structured (organized, filled with patterns, and predictable) and that the power of algorithms resides in their applicability as a tool for routine tasks and in the process of solving mathematics problems.

Part of being able to compute fluently means making smart choices about which tools to use and when. Students should have experiences that help them to choose among mental computation, paper-and-pencil algorithms, estimation, and calculator use. Ability to use algorithms enhances these choices.

References

Carroll, W., & Porter, D. (1998). Alternative algorithms for whole-number operations.

Charles, R., & Lobato, J. (1998). Future basics: Developing mathematical power.

Hiebert, J. (1999). Relationship between research and the NCTM standards.

Kamii, C., & Dominick, A. (1998). The harmful effects of algorithms in grades 1-4.

Kilpatrick, J., Swafford, J., & Findell, B. (Eds.). (2001). Adding it up: Helping children learn mathematics.

National Council of Teachers of Mathematics. (2000). Principles and standards for school mathematics.

Steen, L. A. (1990). On the shoulders of giants: New approaches to numeracy.

What factors contribute most strongly to students' success in learning mathematics?

One of the strongest predictors of students' success is the quality of their teacher.

Research and Best Practice

One of the most important factors contributing to student success is active participation in meaningful mathematics. Students who are actively involved in mathematical modeling, problem solving, and reasoning demonstrate through application the most in-depth understanding of the mathematics being taught. Supporting factors include ample time to perform investigations, classroom practices that emphasize discourse among students and between students and teachers, student reflection on their work, time to revise work, and appreciation of student diversity.

The current instructional practice of covering many discrete topics must change if students are to develop deep understanding and useful performance skills. Teachers who set up active learning tasks that engage students in purposeful work spend substantial time moving about the classroom working with individuals and small groups. They make note of individual student accomplishments and needs, redirect students to new tasks as necessary, and listen as students reason their way through a problem.

Students who experience mathematics in a "user-friendly" classroom environment in which prior knowledge is identified and built upon, and where instruction is developmentally appropriate, are more successful than students who are seated in rows watching, listening, or taking notes on mechanical processes. Students who experience a range of activity from short whole-group instruction to longer times engaged in problem solving are more likely to enjoy learning. A positive student-teacher relationship improves learning.

One of the strongest predictors of students' success is the quality of their teacher. Teachers who are highly qualified with both mathematics content knowledge and pedogological skills are more effective teachers. Teachers who continue their education while teaching tend to develop a deeper understanding of content applications, content knowledge, effective instructional strategies, theoretical bases for instructional decisions, and confidence in decision making. In general, teachers who continue learning throughout their careers are more likely to become conscientious, competent, professional teachers.

Classroom Implications

The teacher's instructional decision making contributes greatly to students' success in their mathematics classes. Those students who approach learning mathematics in realistic contexts, who work as mathematicians do, and who are held to the performance criteria of mathematicians, demonstrate the best understanding of mathematical concepts. Teachers need to consider carefully the mathematics tasks they assign.

Class scheduling is of major importance to both administrators and teachers. Administrators need to examine teacher schedules to facilitate common planning time — a professional collegial time in which teachers design appropriate contextual problem-solving experiences for their students and cooperatively examine student work samples as a means of informing instruction. Teachers must provide classroom time for the in-depth study of major concepts in mathematics. The typical forty-three minute class period does not support the time necessary to explore topics in-depth or from multiple perspectives. Short-segmented class periods often prevent students from achieving the flow and continuity of thinking that is so critical in making sense of mathematics.

Teachers help construct scaffolding for key ideas from students' prior knowledge, anticipate misconceptions, and design learning experiences that build on student thinking and reflect mathematics content aligned with the NCTM *PSSM*. Students need to be engaged in active listening, restating in their own words what was shared by others. Students who are encouraged to try out new ideas, to think aloud, and get specific feedback from others have opportunities to internalize the mathematical concepts they are exploring. Teachers learn from watching and listening to their students and students learn by articulating what they know.

Successful mathmematics students have teachers who stay current in mathematics as well as mathematics education. Effective mathematics teachers

- read and apply relevant research in mathematics pedagogy and education
- keep abreast of changes in mathematics content
- are active members of their professional mathematics education organization

References

Bransford, J. D., Brown, A. L., & Cocking, R. R. (Eds.). (1999). How people learn: Brain, mind, experience, and school.

Darling, L. -H. (1997). The right to learn: A blueprint for creating schools that work.

Gardner, H. T., Toff, B., & Hatch, T. (1996). The age of innocence reconsidered: Preserving the best of the progressive tradition in psychology and education.

Meier, D. (1995). The power of their ideas: Lessons for America from a small school in Harlem.

Sizer, T. (1992). Horace's school: Redesigning the American high school.

Stigler, J. W., & Hiebert, J. (1999). The teaching gap: Best ideas from the world's teachers for improving education in the classroom.

Mathematics For All

Teaching

Assessment

Curriculum

Technology

Learning

How do students' attitudes affect their performance and future opportunities?

Students who enjoy mathematics tend to perform well in their mathematics course work.

Research and Best Practice

Students' attitudes toward mathematics have a great effect on student achievement. Attitudes are stable dispositions, affective responses, or beliefs individuals have that develop largely through experience. Students who enjoy mathematics tend to perform well in their mathematics course work and are more likely to enroll in the more advanced mathematics courses. Conversely, those students who dislike mathematics tend not to do well in these classes, and/or do not attempt the more advanced mathematics classes in secondary school.

Negative attitudes about mathematics are learned, not inherited. Students enter school with a considerable amount of enthusiasm and curiosity that produces mathematical questions such as: What is the distance between my home and school?; How likely am I to win this game?; and Do I have enough paint to finish this project? Students have positive emotions when they make mathematical conjectures, when they make breakthroughs as they solve problems, and when they see connections between important ideas. Of course, students can also experience frustration when not making progress toward solving a problem. Therefore, it is important that instruction provide appropriately challenging problems so students can learn and establish the norm of perseverance for successful problem solving.

A student with a productive attitude finds sense in mathematics, perceives it as both useful and worthwhile, believes that steady effort in learning mathematics pays off, and views him or herself as an effective learner and doer of mathematics. Research suggests that students of color and females often learn early to doubt their mathematical abilities, and as a consequence are more likely to attribute failure to lack of ability. Generally, U.S. students are more likely to attribute success in mathematics problem solving to ability rather than effort. East Asian children, on the other hand, perceive success as a function of effort, not ability. It is important for teachers to model perseverance in the face of challenging problems, and to convey that mistakes and misconceptions are inevitable and provide necessary opportunities for learning. In addition, both students and teachers must believe that all students are endowed with the capabilities to learn mathematics.

Classroom Implications

The practices, culture and norms of classrooms strongly influence student attitudes, particularly during elementary school years, when students' attitudes toward school and academics are forming. Among high poverty students, it was found that an emphasis on conformity, competition, and mathematics as rules produced decreased motivation and achievement compared to a more exploratory curriculum. Students are less likely to think flexibly and critically when their schools emphasize conformity, order, obedience, an acceptance of school and mathematical rules, and a dependence upon the structures provided by these rules. While an organized learning environment is important, promoting students' comfortable exploration of mathematics through challenging open-ended problems should replace classroom norms that emphasize procedures, rules, competition, and speed. However, while fostering students' positive attitudes toward mathematics, teachers need to be careful not to simplify a challenging curriculum or alleviate all of students' frustrations during problem solving.

Successful teachers communicate explicit expectations that students will provide adequate justifications for their answers, persist at problem solving when faced with frustration, and solve problems independently. Students of these teachers show satisfaction and enthusiasm for problem solving and demonstrate an autonomous view of themselves as learners. Effective mathematics teachers establish good relationships with students by being friendly rather than formal, sharing personal anecdotes that illustrate their own problem solving strengths and weaknesses, and establishing systems that hold students accountable for their performance. Most of these teachers emphasize aspects of student performance other than obtaining correct answers. These teachers also tend to use cooperative groups to promote independence and to reduce feelings of frustration in students.

Fostering these desirable classroom norms with low-achieving students can be particularly challenging for teachers, because these students have more difficulty than others at extracting important mathematical ideas from open-ended problems. Nonetheless, teachers have had success at implementing these norms. The teacher practices described above appear to be necessary for successful teaching of ambitious learning goals such as those specified by the NCTM *Principles and Standards for School Mathematics*.

References

Boaler, J. (1997). Experiencing school mathematics: Teaching styles, sex, and setting.

Henningsen, M., & Stein, M. (1997). Mathematical tasks and student cognition: Classroom-based factors that support and inhibit high-level mathematical thinking and reasoning.

Kilpatrick, J., Swafford, J., & Findell, B. (Eds.). (2001). Adding it up: Helping children learn mathematics.

Moses, R., Kamii, M., Swap, S. M., & Howard, J. (1989, November). The algebra project: Organizing in the spirit of Ella.

Schiefele, U., & Csikszentmihalyi, M. (1995). Motivation and ability factors in mathematics experience and achievement.

Mathematics for All

Teaching

Assessment

Curriculum

Technology

Learning

How can teachers help students reflect on and communicate their own learning?

Learning increases after explicit instruction in metacognitive strategies.

Research and Best Practice

Metacognition, sometimes referred to as thinking about thinking, is an excellent way to assist students to reflect on and to communicate their learning. Metacognitive strategies to manage thinking include

- Connecting newly learned information with that already known
- Carefully choosing appropriate thinking strategies for a specific use
- Planning, monitoring, and judging the effectiveness of thinking processes

Learning increases after explicit instruction in metacognitive strategies.

Creating and maintaining portfolios of personal work is one strategy that encourages reflection. The process of selecting and organizing the contents of a portfolio builds self-awareness. The use of classroom portfolios gives students more control over their own learning. It also supports teacher professional development, shifting the emphasis from instruction to facilitation of learning.

Writing is another way for students to discover, organize, summarize, and communicate knowledge. Writing makes thinking processes concrete and increases retention of concepts. The act of writing gives a student access to his or her own thinking processes, enabling the construction of new understandings that are meaningful and applicable.

By facilitating classroom interactions, encouraging students to propose mathematical ideas, helping them learn to evaluate their own thinking and that of others, and developing their reasoning skills, teachers can enhance mathematics learning. Being able to openly discuss and interact with others in the classroom can promote the recognition of connections among concepts and topics and the reorganization of knowledge. When students talk about the strategies they use, teachers can help them build on their informal knowledge.

The use of metacognitive strategies, portfolios, and structured classroom writing assignments supports students' personal construction of mathematics understanding.

Classroom Implications

Metacognitive activities in mathematics classes can ask students to

- Identify what is known and not known (e.g., K-W-L — what I know/want to know/learned)
- Talk about thinking (first through teacher modeling, then in group discussion, culminating in paired problem solving)
- Maintain a thinking journal or learning log (e.g., a process diary)
- Take increased responsibility for planning activities
- Practice targeted self-regulation skills following direct instruction (e.g., estimating time requirements, organizing materials, and scheduling)
- Debrief thinking processes during class closure (e.g., review thinking processes, identify and classify strategies used, evaluate successes, and seek alternatives)
- Participate in guided self-evaluation

Metacognitive strategies, which are most useful when learned responses are inadequate or inappropriate, are developed through frequent challenging problem solving.

Writing tasks must be authentic; that is, the text must address a real audience, sometimes oneself. A journal can be used to reflect on knowledge, feelings, and beliefs. It can open a dialogue between learner and teacher that leads to more individualized instruction and support. Throughout the year, topics for journal writing should start with affective, open-ended prompts (Describe a time when you felt successful in solving a mathematical problem. Why did you feel successful?), proceed to review of familiar mathematics concepts (How did you determine the line of symmetry?), and move toward discussion of more advanced mathematics concepts, to extend and reinforce new understanding.

Other useful types of writing assignments include analytic essays, which develop links between concepts, and concept maps or hierarchical outlines, which can be used to facilitate meaningful cooperative learning, identify misconceptions, evaluate understanding, and demonstrate construction of mathematical knowledge.

References

Association for Supervision and Curriculum Development. (2000). Portfolios: Helping students think about their thinking.

Baxter, J. A., Olson, D., & Woodward, J. (2001, April). Writing in mathematics: The impact on low-achieving students.

Blakey, E., & Spence, S. (1990). Developing metacognition.

Bransford, J. D., Brown, A. L., & Cocking, R. R. (Eds.). (1999). How people learn: Brain, mind, experience, and school.

Dougiamas, M. (1999). Reading and writing for Internet teaching.

National Council of Teachers of Mathematics. (2000). Principles and standards for school mathematics.

Willis, S. (2000). Portfolios: Helping students think about their thinking.

Wolfe, P. (2001). Brain matters: Translating research into classroom practice.

What role does active hands-on learning play in mathematics instruction?

Use of manipulatives is essential and effective in both elementary and secondary instruction.

Research and Best Practice

Mathematical learning in young children is strongly linked to sense perception and concrete experience. Children move toward an understanding of symbols, and eventually abstract concepts, only after they have first experienced ideas on a concrete level.

Mathematics achievement is increased through the long-term use of concrete instructional materials and active lessons at various grade levels. The more avenues there are to receive data through the senses, the more connections the brain can make. The more connections that are made, the better a learner can understand a new idea. This holds not only for primary age learners, but through adulthood. All students need to approach the learning of mathematics by actively doing mathematics. This includes such activities as physically measuring objects, collecting and representing data, and handling geometric solids from the earliest ages. Other active learning experiences are representing numbers with locking cubes to put together and take apart groups of tens, sorting objects or cards containing pictures of shapes or mathematical objects, or using tiles to represent algebraic quantities. Students also enjoy "acting out" problems or equations.

Students do not discover or understand mathematical concepts simply by manipulating concrete materials. Mathematics teachers must intervene frequently as part of the instructional process to help students focus on underlying mathematical ideas and to help build bridges from the students' active work to their corresponding work with mathematical symbols or actions. It is important that students frequently reflect on their actions in relation to the mathematical concepts the teacher is promoting and the constraints of the task as they conceive it.

Despite the known benefits of hands-on learning, many mathematics teachers do not take full advantage of this strategy's effectiveness for learning. While most mathematics teachers have access to a variety of manipulatives, they incorporate them into their lessons with varying frequency, and some do not use them at all.

Classroom Implications

The kinds of experiences teachers provide clearly play a major role in determining the extent and quality of a student's learning. Students' understanding will increase if they are actively engaged in tasks and experiences designed to deepen and connect their knowledge of mathematical concepts. Individual students learn in different ways. Through the use of manipulatives, various senses are brought into play. When students can touch and move objects to make visual representation of mathematical concepts, different learning modalities are addressed.

There is no single best method for mathematics instruction. However, we do know that any mathematics topic should be presented involving multiple instructional techniques, allowing all students to develop a mathematical understanding through at least one method. For example, by presenting an activity with three components (manipulatives, technology, and formalizing), we not only give students with varied learning styles different ways to see a problem, we give them extra time to process the concept.

Using manipulatives in combination with other instructional methods can enrich and deepen students' understanding. Appropriate use of concrete materials should be one component of a comprehensive mathematics education program.

References

Germain, Y. -M. (1991). Bringing the NCTM standards to life: Exemplary practices from high-schools.

National Council of Teachers of Mathematics. (2000). Principles and standards for school mathematics.

Sowell, E. J. (1989). Effects of manipulative materials in mathematics instruction.

Mathematics For All

Teaching

Assessment

Curriculum

Technology

Learning

How does using contextual or applied activities improve student learning in mathematics?

Classroom activities with application to real world situations are the lessons students seem to learn from and appreciate the most.

Research and Best Practice

Teachers have always sensed that classroom activities with application to real-world situations are the lessons their students seem to learn from and appreciate the most. Students have more meaningful learning experiences when the concepts have a personal connection to their own lives, beyond a textbook or resource narrative.

Brain research studies shed light on why this may be the case. Brain research demonstrates that:

- The more senses used in instruction, the better learners will be able to remember, retrieve, and connect the information in their memories.
- Physical experiences or meaningful contexts can provide learners with strong blocks for building knowledge.
- If new knowledge is connected to what learners already know, the acquisition of the new knowledge is enhanced.

Information about memory creation and storage, learning, and complex connections provides an explanation for the success of students' learning through hands-on contextual activities.

At the elementary level many teachers have used manipulative materials to provide this contextual setting. The old saying, "I hear and I forget; I see and I remember; I do and I understand", has been the hallmark in elementary education for many years and is supported by brain research. Students learn best when doing. Older students need similar experiences that involve physical materials or at least real-life contextual settings.

By incorporating realistic, integrated, or interdisciplinary activities that build on established knowledge and skills and more than one sense (seeing, hearing, or touching), memory pathways become more easily accessed and cross-referenced for future use. As the learner ages, the ease of access of learning pathways is directly dependent on stimulation from prior learning. Concepts embedded this way are truly learned.

Classroom Implications

Since hands-on contextual activities help learning, teachers should include such activities in their lessons. If manipulative materials help to illustrate a new concept, use them. Young children may gain a better feeling for place value by chip trading or exchanging ten blue markers for one red marker or vice versa. Older students may gain a better understanding of solving an algebraic equation by working with manipulatives to physically build a representation of the equation, then solve it through movement of the pieces.

Since real life applied activities help learning, teachers should try to include a contextual setting for many of their lessons. In some cases the setting can motivate learning the concept, while in other cases it can illustrate it. Students' learning may be enhanced if they use their prior knowledge to construct and refine a new concept. For example, students trying to determine which school candidate has the best chance of winning the class presidency can conduct a valid survey by calling upon their knowledge of random selection and probabilities.

Sources of problem based learning curricula and authentic assessments are becoming widely available. Real-time data is now available on the Internet. Lessons can be developed that use the interest of the students to naturally make the connections between foundational concepts and an application.

Teachers might experiment with interdisciplinary applications as action research projects in the classroom. The teacher can develop a hypothesis for successful impact, implement the lesson, collect the data from students' performance, and analyze the data to see if such a lesson had the desired result.

Understanding the learning process can become a fascinating study for all teachers. As teachers discover the most effective strategies for better student achievement, they can adapt their lessons accordingly. Brain research will continue to progress and will no doubt give us more information on how to better prepare lessons for maximum student success.

References

Caine, R. N., & Caine, G. (1994). Making connections: Teaching and the human brain.

Nunley, K. F. (1999). The regular educator's guide to the brain.

Mathematics For All

Teaching

Assessment

Curriculum

Technology

Learning

What can parents do to support student learning in mathematics?

Parent involvement is not effective if available only as an afterthought.

Research and Best Practice

The effectiveness of parent involvement in increasing student achievement and success has been a subject of much research. When a school or district implements a well-designed and planned parent involvement effort, all students benefit, regardless of race, ethnicity, or income. Such a program has been found to be the most accurate predictor of student achievement and success.

The National PTA recognizes parents as the primary influence in a student's life and a necessary partner in their education. Parent involvement means that the parents or guardians of a student are participating actively in a child's education. It ranges from volunteering in a student's classroom to reading with them before bedtime to assuming leadership through participation on school committees.

Parent involvement is not effective if available only as an afterthought. Inclusion of parents requires a planned and well-coordinated effort, which takes time. Time is so valuable to educators that planning parent involvement programs may not be a priority. The benefits of a well-coordinated parent involvement program include: higher grades; better attendance; consistent completion of homework; higher graduation rates; decreased alcohol use, violence, and antisocial behavior; and greater support and ratings of teachers by parents and community.

Successful parent involvement programs contain components that are addressed in the National PTA's standards for parent/family involvement programs. These standards address identified best practices. They are (1) Communicating — meaningful and consistent communication between home and school; (2) Parenting — support of parent training focused on parenting skills and current education topics; (3) Student Learning — active participation in student learning at home; (4) Volunteering — varied and meaningful volunteer opportunities; (5) School Decision Making and Advocacy — full partnership in decisions and actions affecting children and families; and (6) Collaborating with Community — use of community resources to enhance student learning, and school-family partnerships. These standards assist educators, parents, and the community in developing or improving parent involvement programs within the context of locally identified needs.

Classroom Implications

Parents and children can enjoy mathematics together. With the proper resources and information, parents, families, and the community can become a teacher's greatest asset and support system. Communication is critical to the success of any relationship. It is important for schools to begin communicating with parents early in the school year. Although most schools have open houses, a school could give parents an orientation to all of the opportunities available throughout the school year, including a brief introduction to standards, how parents can contact school staff and administration if they have concerns, and how different subjects are taught.

Family Math and EQUALS have excellent programs to show parents how to encourage mathematics learning and problem solving. The U.S. Department of Education and the National Science Foundation publish free parent resources that could be sent home with children. If using a non-traditional mathematics program, involve parents in doing the activities to illustrate the mathematics content and processes their student is learning. After this experience, most parents become advocates and spread their enthusiasm to others.

A child's homework project is more likely to be completed when parents find the activity relevant to their child's education and are provided with assistive guidelines. When the teacher follows up with the parents on how the activity went, student learning is further supported. Many mathematics curricula and programs offer ideas for take-home activities and for two-way contact with parents.

Volunteering has traditionally meant direct participation on-site, including doing presentations or participating on a Career Day panel. To increase participation, volunteering could include activities done at home, such as calling Career Day panelists or creating presentation visuals. When alternatives are provided to on-site volunteering, more parents can participate, positively affecting how students view education.

Parents can be vital to decision making and advocacy work for schools. They could be given the opportunity to help write proposals for additional funding for school programs. Partnerships enrich educational experiences both in content and context. Schools and local informal education facilities (e.g., zoo, planetarium) could develop curricula together. Community members could be mentors for mathematics careers, and businesses could allow a few hours a year for employed parents to volunteer or attend school conferences.

References

Baker, A., & Soden, L. (1998). The challenges of parent involvement research.

Burns, M. (2000). About teaching mathematics: A K–8 resource.

Cotton, K., & Wikelund, K. R. (1989, May). Parent involvement in education. Close-Up #6.

Espinosa, L. M. (May 1995). Hispanic parent involvement in early childhood programs.

Flood, J. (1993). The relationship between parent involvement and student achievement: A review of the literature.

Fromboluti, C. S., & Rinck, N. (1999). Early childhood: Where learning begins — mathematics.

Maynard, S., & Howley, A. (June 1997). Parent and community involvement in rural schools.

National Action Council for Minorities in Engineering. (2001, December). Math is power: What every parent needs to know.

National Center for Education Statistics. (1998, January). Parent involvement in children's education: Efforts by public elementary schools.

National Council of Teachers of Mathematics. (2001). Figure this! Math challenges for families: Helping your child learn math.

National Parent Teacher Association. (1997). National PTA's national standards for parent/family involvement programs.

Yale Child Study Center, Comer School Development Program. (2001). Program overview: The parent team.

Mathematics For All

Teaching

Assessment

Curriculum

Technology

Learning

What are characteristics of effective homework in mathematics?

The home should be a place to extend mathematics learning.

Research and Best Practice

Daily, children hurry home from school and arrive to face the obligatory question from parents, "What did you learn in school today?" They return to school the following day, and their teacher asks, "Do you have your homework assignment?" Perhaps a better question would be "What did you learn at home?" The home should be a place to extend mathematics learning.

Student learning in mathematics should always focus on understanding the set of skills and knowledge needed to investigate the world. Homework must emphasize developing students' mathematics skills to solve problems, which will help them understand the world. These mathematics skills are described as "process skills" in the NCTM *Principles and Standards for School Mathematics* and "habits of mind" in *Benchmarks for Science Literacy*. Mathematics educators and mathematicians agree that knowing mathematics is more than being able to recall facts. Research indicates that individuals with expertise in mathematics understand mathematics concepts, how to apply them to challenging, non-routine real-life problem-solving situations, and how to learn from their own problem-solving efforts.

Homework assignments provide the opportunity for students to do long-term projects that require multiple levels of understanding. Students take ownership when they spend weeks following stock prices in the newspaper, paying close attention to favorites, predicting industry trends, interviewing traders, or perhaps even participating in an investment club. Watching TV and timing commercial breaks one night may be interesting, but when students keep data over a few weeks — timing commercials in different types of programs, making charts, and drawing graphs — their learning will go beyond the curriculum.

Homework time is an opportunity for students to reflect on learning and synthesize their mathematics understandings. Well-designed homework can bring parents and other adults into a student's community of mathematics learners. Assignments should include students discussing their learning with others. This can be done through student learning teams, parent involvement, or the teacher using e-mail to have discussion groups. Mathematics is in every aspect of life. Teachers should take advantage of the opportunity to provide students with authentic learning opportunities at home.

Classroom Implications

The value placed on various aspects of mathematics learning can be seen in the allocation of instructional time in class and by the nature of homework assigned. Teachers who value problem-solving skills will provide time in class to develop students' ability to solve problems and then will assign homework that uses these skills in new settings. What goes on in class should match the homework assigned.

Mathematics homework should not be schoolwork done at home. The home provides a unique opportunity for students to gain mathematics understanding by solving mathematics problems. Placing the major emphasis on basic skills and drill for skill development in mathematics is somewhat of a waste of student, parent, and teacher time and effort.

Teaching for understanding requires carefully designed tasks. Homework assignments should have clear criteria and/or written rubrics that describe expectations and establish student goals. The teacher must be certain that students have access to the materials and resources they will need to complete the assignment.

It is important for students to do their best, and for teachers to examine student work. Less is often more when it comes to homework. A product that has been refined by the student results in more effective learning than a large volume of work completed with little thought. The quality of student work is often determined by the standards a teacher sets on the assignment, time spent reviewing the expectations, and suggestions for improvements. A homework assignment should be a major event in student learning. Selling students on the importance of an assignment as a learning event is important: their ownership will determine the depth and breadth of their learning.

References

American Association for the Advancement of Science, Project 2061. (1993). Benchmarks for science literacy.

National Council of Teachers of Mathematics. (2000). Principles and standards for school mathematics.

National Science Foundation. (1999). Inquiry thoughts, views, and strategies for the K–5 classroom.

Perkins, D. (1993). Learning for understanding.

What is the impact of teacher learning on student learning?

> *"Teachers need to understand the big ideas of mathematics and be able to represent mathematics as a coherent and connected enterprise. Their decisions and their actions in the classroom — all of which affect how well their students learn mathematics — should be based on this knowledge."*
>
> National Council of Teachers of Mathematics, 2000, p. 17.

Research and Best Practice

One of the strongest predictors of students' success is the quality of their teacher. Highly qualified teachers with both mathematics content knowledge and pedagogical skills are more effective. Teachers who continue to learn tend to develop a deeper understanding of content applications, content knowledge, effective instructional strategies, theoretical bases for instructional decisions, and confidence in decision making. Teachers who continue learning throughout their careers are more likely to become reflective, competent, professional teachers.

Mathematics teachers who are leading students to explore ideas, pose conjectures, and explain their reasoning need robust understanding of the subject. Teachers who use a more inquiry-based approach and who create learning communities need a deep, connected understanding of mathematical concepts in order to facilitate student learning. Comfortable with their own understanding, they can anticipate and respond to student misconceptions as well as student insights. Without this understanding, teachers are limited by their own misconceptions, often the same ones entertained by their students. Furthermore, to select mathematical tasks that enable all students to grow mathematically, they need a deep sense of how each task relates to other tasks, to prior learning, and to future concepts.

Many studies have explored teacher knowledge as evidenced in mathematics achievement tests and formal coursework. More recent studies have begun to connect a teacher's knowledge of mathematics and ability to teach mathematics effectively with student achievement. Four critical teacher characteristics and behaviors are:

- Deep understanding of mathematics — concepts, practices, principles, representations, and applications
- Deep understanding of the ways children learn mathematics
- Implementation of methods that draw out and build upon student mathematical thinking
- Continual engagement in reflective practice

The Teaching Principle of the NCTM *Principles and Standards for School Mathematics* emphasizes the importance of teacher preparation and continual professional growth for achieving student understanding of mathematics.

Classroom Implications

A community of learners includes a teacher who is a learner with students. Mathematics education standards that establish goals for students to attain lifelong learning skills should, and do, expect as much of teachers.

Teacher learning specific to the mathematics subject matter provides teachers with both the understanding to anticipate and overcome student mathematics misconceptions and the confidence to teach in an inquiry mode. A job-embedded opportunity for such subject matter learning occurs while teaching a rich, conceptually-based mathematics program. Teachers become both students and teachers of the mathematics content. A broad understanding of mathematics provides teachers with one of the key components for the integration of the various strands of mathematics as well as integration across the curriculum.

Teachers should make decisions based upon data; the best data for teachers to use is the information that is gathered in the classroom. Teachers who are learners engage in action research to hone their instructional decision making skills. Data collected in the classroom provide evidence that can be used in making instructional adjustments.

Mathematics teachers should stay current in mathematics as well as mathematics education. Reviewing the growth of knowledge in any area of mathematics makes it clear that continued learning is necessary. One way professional teachers maintain a current knowledge of their content area is through memberships in professional organizations. These organizations provide journals that synthesize current topics in mathematics and mathematics education.

Perhaps the most significant result of teachers being engaged in learning is the enthusiasm for learning brought to the classroom. Students know when a teacher is excited about learning. This adds to students' interest and enthusiasm for learning.

References

Cohen, D. K., & Hill, H. C. (1998). Instructional policy and classroom performance: The mathematics reform in California.

Darling, L. -H., & Ball, D. L. (2000). Teaching for high standards: What policymakers need to know and be able to do.

Johnson, J. (2000). Teaching and learning mathematics: Using research to shift from the "yesterday" mind to the "tomorrow" mind.

Ma, L. (1999). Knowing and teaching elementary mathematics: Teachers' understanding of fundamental mathematics in China and the United States.

National Council of Teachers of Mathematics. (2000). Principles and standards for school mathematics.

Wenglinsky, H. (2000). How teaching matters: Bringing the classroom back into discussions of teacher quality.

Mathematics For All

Teaching

Assessment

Curriculum

Technology

Learning

References

American Association for the Advancement of Science, Project 2061. (1993). *Benchmarks for science literacy.* New York: Oxford University Press.

American Psychological Association (APA). (1997). *Learner-centered psychological principles.* Retrieved January 23, 2002, from the APA Web site: http://www.apa.org/ed/lcp2/lcp14.html

Anderson, J., & Adams, M. (1992). Acknowledging the learning styles of diverse student populations: Implications for instructional design. In L. Chism (Ed.), *New directions in teaching and learning. No. 42. Teaching for diversity* (pp. 19-33). San Francisco, CA: Jossey-Bass.

Anderson, R. (1996). *Study of curriculum reform.* Washington, DC: U.S. Department of Education, Office of Educational Research and Improvement.

Anderson, R. C., Hiebert, E. H., Scott, J. A., & Wilkinson, I. A. G. (1984). *Becoming a nation of readers: The report of the Commission on Reading.* Washington, DC: The National Institute of Education.

Apthorp, H. S., Bodrova, E., Dean, C. B., & Florian, J. E. (2001). *Noteworthy perspectives. Teaching to the core: Reading, writing, and mathematics.* Aurora, CO: Mid-continent Research for Education and Learning.

Armstrong, T. (1994). *Multiple intelligences in the classroom.* Alexandria, VA: Association for Supervision and Curriculum Development.

Armstrong, T. (1998). *Awakening genius in the classroom.* Alexandria, VA: Association for Supervision and Curriculum Development.

Association for Supervision and Curriculum Development. (2000). Portfolios: Helping students think about their thinking. *Education Update, 42*(4), 7.

Association of State Supervisors of Mathematics, & National Council of Supervisors of Mathematics. (1993). *Guide to selecting instructional materials for mathematics education.* Washington, DC: Author.

Australian Association of Mathematics Teachers (AAMT). (1996). *Statement on the use of technology for mathematics in Australian schools.* Retrieved January 23, 2002, from the AAMT Web site: http://www.aamt.edu.au/policies/Tech_St.pdf

Bailey, T. (1997). Integrating vocational and academic education. In *High school mathematics at work.* Washington, DC: National Academy Press.

Baker, A., & Soden, L. (1998). *The challenges of parent involvement research.* New York: ERIC Clearinghouse on Urban Education. (ERIC Document Reproduction Service No. ED419030).

Ball, D. L. (1997). Developing mathematics reform: What don't we know about teacher learning—but would make good working hypotheses. In S. N. Friel & G. W. Bright (Eds.), *Reflecting on our work: NSF teacher enhancement in K-6 mathematics* (pp. 77-111). New York: University Press of America.

Bandura, A., & Adams, N. E. (1977). Analysis of self-efficacy theory of behavioral change. *Cognitive Therapy & Research, 1,* 287-310.

Barton, M. L., & Heidema, C. (2002). *Teaching reading in mathematics.* (2nd ed.). Aurora, CO: Mid-continent Research for Education and Learning.

Battista, M. T. (1994). Teacher beliefs and the reform movement in mathematics education. *Phi Delta Kappan, 75*(6), 462.

Baxter, J. A., Olson, D., & Woodward, J. (2001, April). *Writing in mathematics: The impact on low-achieving students.* Paper presented at the annual meeting of the American Educational Research Association, Seattle, WA.

Beck, S. E. (1997, July). *The good, the bad and the ugly or why it's a good idea to evaluate web sources?* Retrieved January 23, 2002, from New Mexico State University Web site http://lib.nmsu.edu/instruction/eval.html

Billmeyer, R., & Barton, M. L. (1998). *Teaching reading in the content areas.* (2nd ed.). Aurora, CO: Mid-continent Research for Education and Learning.

Blakey, E., & Spence, S. (1990). *Developing metacognition.* Syracuse, NY: ERIC Clearinghouse on Information Resources. (ERIC Document Reproduction Service No. ED327218).

Boaler, J. (1997). *Experiencing school mathematics: Teaching styles, sex, and setting.* Buckingham, UK: Open University Press.

References

Bransford, J. D., Brown, A. L., & Cocking, R. R. (Eds.). (1999). *How people learn: Brain, mind, experience, and school.* Washington, DC: National Academy Press.

Britton, E., Huntley, M. A., Jacobs, G., & Weinberg, A. S. (1999). *Connecting mathematics and science to workplace contexts: A guide to curriculum materials.* Thousand Oaks, CA: Corwin Press.

Brooks, J. G., & Brooks, M. G. (1993). *In search of understanding: The case for constructivist classrooms.* Alexandria, VA: Association for Supervision and Curriculum Development.

Brophy, J. E. (1991). Conclusions to advances in research on teaching. Volume 2: Teachers' knowledge of subject matter as it relates to their teaching practice. In J. E. Brophy (Ed.), *Advances in research on teaching: Teachers' subject matter knowledge and classroom instruction* (pp. 347-362). Greenwich, CT: JAI Press, Inc.

Brown, J., Collins, A., & Duguid, P. (1989). Situated cognition and the culture of learning. *Educational Researcher, 18*, 32-42.

Burke, M. J., & Curcio, F. R. (Eds.). (2000). *Learning mathematics for a new century. 2000 yearbook.* Reston, VA: National Council of Teachers of Mathematics.

Burns, M. (2000). *About teaching mathematics: A K–8 resource.* White Plains, NY: Math Solutions Publications.

Caine, R. N., & Caine, G. (1994). *Making connections: Teaching and the human brain.* Menlo Park, CA: Addison-Wesley.

Campbell, P. (1992). *Math, science, and your daughter: What can parents do? Encouraging girls in math and science series.* Washington, DC: Office of Educational Research and Improvement, U.S. Department of Education.

Campbell, P., & Kreinberg, N. (1998). *Moving into the mainstream: From equity as a separate concept to high quality includes all.* Washington, DC: National Science Foundation. Collaboration for Equity Fairness in Science and Mathematics Education.

Carroll, W., & Porter, D. (1998). Alternative algorithms for whole-number operations. In L. J. Morrow (Ed.), *The teaching and learning of algorithms in school mathematics. 1998 yearbook* (pp. 106-114). Reston, VA: National Council of Teachers of Mathematics.

Cawelti, G. (Ed.). (1999). *Handbook of research on improving student achievement.* Arlington, VA: Educational Research Service.

Charles, R., & Lobato, J. (1998). *Future basics: Developing mathematical power* (National Council of Supervisors of Mathematics Monograph). Golden, CO: National Council of Supervisors of Mathematics.

Clarke, D. (1997). *Constructive assessment in mathematics: Practical steps for classroom teachers.* Berkeley, CA: Key Curriculum Press.

Clements, D. H., & McMillen, S. (1996). Rethinking concrete manipulatives. *Teaching Children Mathematics, 3*(5), 270-279.

Cohen, D. K., & Hill, H. C. (1998). *Instructional policy and classroom performance: The mathematics reform in California.* (CPRE Research Report Series, RR-39). Phiadelpphia, PA: University of Pennsylvania,Consortium for Policy Research in Education.

Colburn, W. (1821). *Intellectual arithmetic, upon the inductive method of instruction.* Boston MA: Reynolds & Co. Boston.

Collins, A. M. (2000). Yours is not to reason why, just plug in the numbers and multiply. *Education Week, 20*(1), 62.

Collins, A. M. (Ed.). (2000). So, what questions should I ask to further student understanding? *Partnerships Promoting Student Achievement in Mathematics, 2*(1).

Comer, J. P. (1985). The Yale-New Haven Primary Prevention Project: A follow-up study. *Journal of the American Academy of Child Psychiatry, 23*(2), 154-60.

Corwin, R. B., Storeygard, J., & Price. S. L. (1995). *Talking mathematics: Supporting children's voices.* Portsmouth, NH: Heinemann.

Cotton, K., & Wikelund, K. R. (1989, May). *Parent involvement in education. Close-Up #6.* Retrieved January 23, 2002, from Northwest Regional Educational Laboratory, School Improvement Research Series (SIRS), Web site: http://www.nwrel.org/scpd/sirs/3/cu6.html

Cradler, J. (n.d.). *Summary of current research and evaluation findings on technology in education.* Retrieved January 24, 2002, from the WestEd Web site: http://www.wested.org/techpolicy/refind.html

References

Cuevas, G., & Driscoll, M. (Eds.). (1993). *Reaching all students with mathematics*. Reston, VA: National Council of Teachers of Mathematics.

Cuoco, A. A. (Ed.). (2001). *The roles of representation in school mathematics. 2001 yearbook*. Reston, VA: National Council of Teachers of Mathematics.

Darling, L. -H. (1994). National standards and assessments: Will they improve education? *American Journal of Education, 102*(4), 478-510.

Darling, L. -H. (1997). *The right to learn: A blueprint for creating schools that work*. San Francisco, CA: Jossey-Bass.

Darling, L. -H. (Ed.). (1994). *Professional development schools*. New York: Teachers College Press.

Darling, L. -H., & Ball, D. L. (2000). *Teaching for high standards: What policymakers need to know and be able to do*. (CPRE paper. No. JRE-04). Philadelphia, PA: University of Pennsylvania, Consortium for Policy Research in Education.

DeCorte, E. Greer, B., & Verschaffel, L. (1996). Mathematics teaching and learning. In D. C. Berliner & R. C. Calfee (Eds.), *Handbook of educational psychology* (pp. 491-549). New York: Macmillan.

Delgado, C. -G. (1991). Involving parents in the schools: A process of empowerment. *American Journal of Education, 100*, 20-46.

Demana, F., & Waits, B. (1990). Enhancing mathematics teaching and learning through technology. In T. Cooney & C. Hirsch (Eds.), *Teaching and learning mathematics in the 1990s* (pp. 212-222). Reston, VA: National Council of Teachers of Mathematics.

Dougiamas, M. (1999, June). *Reading and writing for Internet teaching*. Retrieved January 24, 2002, from http://dougiamas.com/writing/readwrite.html

Dowker, A. (1992). Computational strategies of professional mathematicians. *Journal for Research in Mathematics Education, 23*(1), 45-55.

Duckworth, E. (1987). *The having of wonderful ideas and other essays on teaching and learning*. New York: Teachers College Press.

Dunn, R. (1996). *How to implement and supervise a learning style program*. Alexandria, VA: Association for Supervision and Curriculum Development.

Dunn, R., & Griggs, S. (1995). *Multiculturalism and learning style: Teaching and counseling adolescents*. Westport, CT: Praeger.

Edmonds, R. R., & Frederiksen, J. R. (1978). *Search for effective schools: The identification and analysis of city schools that are instructionally effective for poor children*. Cambridge, MA: Harvard University Center for Urban Studies.

Eisenhower National Clearinghouse for Mathematics and Science Education. (1998). *Ideas that work: Mathematics professional development*. Columbus, OH: Author.

Elliott, P. C. (Ed.). (1990). *Communication in mathematics: K–12 and beyond. 1990 yearbook*. Reston, VA: National Council of Teachers of Mathematics.

Espinosa, L. M. (1995, May). *Hispanic parent involvement in early childhood programs*. Champaign, IL: ERIC Clearinghouse on Elementary and Early Childhood Education. (ERIC Document Reproduction Service No. EDO-PS-95-3).

Felder, R. (1996). Matters of style. *ASEE Prism, 6*(4), 18-23.

Fennema, E., & Franke, M. L. (1992). Teachers' knowledge and its impact. In Douglas Grouws (Ed.), *Handbook of research on mathematics teaching and learning* (pp. 147-164). New York: Macmillan.

Fennema, E., & Romberg, T. A. (Eds.). (1999). *Mathematics classrooms that promote understanding*. Mahwah, NJ: Lawrence Erlbaum.

Ferrini, J. G. -M., Johnson, L., & Mills, G. (Eds.). (1998). *Making change in mathematics education: Learning from the field*. Reston, VA: National Council of Teachers of Mathematics.

Flood, J. (1993). *The relationship between parent involvement and student achievement: A review of the literature*. (ERIC Document Reproduction Service No. ED357848).

Frand, J. L. (2000). The information-age mindset. *Educause Review, 35*(5), 15-24.

Froelich, G. (1991). *Connecting mathematics*. Reston, VA: National Council of Teachers of Mathematics.

Fromboluti, C. S., & Rinck, N. (1999, June). *Early childhood: Where learning begins – mathematics*. Retrieved January 24, 2002, from the U.S. Department of Education Web site: http://www.ed.gov/pubs/EarlyMath/title.htmll

References

Fullan, M. G. (1991). *The new meaning of educational change*. New York: Teachers College Press.

Fuson, K. C. (1992). Research on learning and teaching addition and subtraction of whole numbers. In G. Leinhardt, R. T. Putnam, & R. A. Hattrup (Eds.), *The analysis of arithmetic for mathematics teaching* (pp. 53-187). Hillsdale, NJ: Lawrence Erlbaum.

Gardner, H. T. (1993). *Multiple intelligences: The theory into practice*. New York: Basic Books.

Gardner, H. T., Toff, B., & Hatch, T. (1996). The age of innocence reconsidered: Preserving the best of the progressive tradition in psychology and education. In D. R. Olson & N. Torrance (Eds.), *The handbook of education and human development: New models of learning, teaching, and schooling* (pp. 28-55). Cambridge, MA: Blackwell.

Garet, M. S., Porter, A. C., Desimone, L., & Birman, B. F. (2001). What makes professional development effective? Results from a national sample of teachers. *American Educational Research Journal, 38*(4), 915-945.

Germain, Y. -M. (1991). *Bringing the NCTM standards to life: Exemplary practices from high-schools*. Larchmont, NY: Eye on Education.

Glatthorn, A. (1998). *Performance assessment and standards-based curricula: The achievement cycle*. Larchmont, NY: Eye on Education.

Goldsmith, L. T., Mark, J., & Kantrov, I. (1998). *Choosing a standards-based mathematics curriculum*. Newton, MA: Educational Development Center, Inc.

Groves, S., & Stacey, K. (1998). Calculators in primary mathematics: Exploring number before teaching algorithms. In L. J. Morrow (Ed.), *The teaching and learning of algorithms in school mathematics. 1998 yearbook*. Reston, VA: National Council of Teachers of Mathematics.

Grunow, J. E. (1999). *Using concept maps in a professional development program to assess and enhance teachers' understanding* (UMI #9910421). Ann Arbor, MI: University of Michigan.

Grunow, J. E. (2001). *Planning curriculum in mathematics*. Madison, WI: Wisconsin Departnment of Public Instruction.

Harris, J. L. (Ed.). (1998). Informal mathematics and science education, *ENC Focus, 5*(2).

Haycock, K. (1998, Fall). Good teaching matters ... a lot. *Magazine of History, 13*(1), 61-63.

Hembree, R., & Dessart, D. (1986). Effects of hand held calculators in pre-college mathematics education: A meta-analysis. *Journal for Research in Mathematics Education, 17*, 83-89.

Henningsen, M., & Stein, M. (1997). Mathematical tasks and student cognition: Classroom-based factors that support and inhibit high-level mathematical thinking and reasoning. *Journal for Research in Mathematics Education, 28*(5), 524-549.

Hiebert, J. (1999). Relationship between research and the NCTM standards. *Journal of Research in Mathematics Education, 30*(1), 3-19.

Hiebert, J., & Carpenter, T. P. (1992). Learning and teaching with understanding. In D. Grouws (Ed), *Handbook of research on mathematics teaching and learning* (pp. 65-97). New York: Macmillan.

Hiebert, J., Carpenter, T. P., Fennema, E., Fuson, K. C., Kearne, D., Murray, H., Olivier, A., & Human, P. (1997). *Making sense: Teaching and learning mathematics with understanding*. Portsmouth, NH: Heinemann.

Hiebert, J., Carpenter, T. P., Fennema, E., Fuson, K., Murray, H., Oliver, A., Human, P., & Wearne, D. (1997). *Designing classrooms for learning mathematics with understanding*. Portsmouth, NH: Heinemann.

Hoachlander, G. (1997). Organizing mathematics education around work. In L. Steen (Ed.), *Why numbers count: Quantitative literacy for tomorrow's America* (pp. 122-136). New York: College Board.

Hoffman, K. M., & Stage, E. K. (1993). Science for all students. *Educational Leadership, 50*(5), 27-31.

Hyde, A. (2001, December). *Another myth about math*. Retrieved January 24, 2002, from the North Central Regional Educational Laboratory Web site: http://www.ncrel.org/mands/docs/7-3.htm

International Society for Technology in Education. (2000). *National educational technology standards for students: Connecting curriculum and technology*. Eugene, OR: Author.

International Technology Education Association (ITEA). (2000). *Standards for technological literacy: Content for the study of technology*. Retrieved January 24, 2002, from ITEA Web site: http://www.iteawww.org/TAA/PDF/xstnd.pdf

Jensen, E. (1998). *Teaching with the brain in mind*. Alexandria, VA: Association for Supervision and Curriculum Development.

References

Johnson, J. (2000). *Teaching and learning mathematics: Using research to shift from the "yesterday" mind to the "tomorrow" mind.* Olympia, WA: Resource Center, Office of the Superintendent of Public Instruction, Resource Center.

Joyner, J., & Bright, G. (1998). *Focusing on classroom assessment.* Greensboro, NC: University of North Carolina at Greensboro, Center for School Accountability and Staff Development.

Kamii, C., & Dominick, A. (1998). The harmful effects of algorithms in grades 1-4. In L. Morrow (Ed.), *The teaching and learning of algorithms in school mathematics* (pp. 130-140). Reston, VA: National Council of Teachers of Mathematics.

Kelley, M. (1985). The effect of the use of the hand-held calculator on the development of problem-solving strategies. *Dissertation Abstracts International, 41,* 3751A.

Kilpatrick, J., Swafford, J., & Findell, B. (Eds.). (2001). *Adding it up: Helping children learn mathematics.* Washington, DC: National Academy Press.

Kimmins, D., & Bouldin, E. (1996, March). *Teaching the prospective teacher: Making mathematics come alive with technology.* Paper presented at the seventh Annual Conference on College Teaching and Learning, Jacksonville, FL.

Kulm, G. (Ed.). (1990). *Assessing higher order thinking in mathematics.* Washington, DC: American Association for the Advancement of Science.

Land, S. M., & Greene, B. A. (2000). Project-based learning with the World Wide Web: A qualitative study of resource integration. *Educational Technology Research and Development, 48*(1), 45-67.

Leadership and the New Technologies. (1999, March/April). *News briefs. 1999 Research report on the effectiveness of technology in schools. LNT Perspectives, 8.* Retrieved January 24, 2002, from the Leadership and the New Technologies Web site: http://www.edc.org/LNT/news/Issue8/brief2.htm

Leinhardt, G., Zaslavsky, O., & Stein, M. K. (1990). Functions, graphs, and graphing: Tasks, learning, and teaching. *Review of Educational Research, 60*(1), 1-64.

Leinwand, S. (1995, June 4). It's time to abandon computational drudgery, but not the computation [Perspective]. *San Jose Mercury News,* pp. 1F, 8F.

Loucks, S. -H., Hewson, P. W., Love, N., & Stiles, K. (Eds.). (1998). *Designing professional development for teachers of science and mathematics.* Thousand Oaks, CA: Corwin Press.

Ma, L. (1999). *Knowing and teaching elementary mathematics: Teachers' understanding of fundamental mathematics in China and the United States.* Mahwah, NJ: Lawrence Erlbaum.

Marzano, R. J., & Kendall, J. S. (1996). *A comprehensive guide to designing standards-based districts, schools, and classrooms.* Alexandria, VA: Association for Supervision and Curriculum Development.

Marzano, R. J., Pickering, D. J., & Pollock, J. E. (2001). *Classroom instruction that works: Research-based strategies for increasing student achievement.* Alexandria, VA: Association for Supervision and Curriculum Development.

Maynard, S., & Howley, A. (June 1997). *Parent and community involvement in rural schools.* ERIC Clearinghouse on Rural Education and Small Schools. (ERIC Document Reproduction Service No EDO-RC-97-3).

McKeachie, W. J. (1995, November). Learning styles can become learning strategies. *The National Teaching & Learning Forum, 4*(6). Retrieved January 24, 2002, from The National Teaching & Learning Forum Web site: http://www.ntlf.com/html/pi/9511/article1.htm

McLaughlin, M. W., & Talbert, J. E. (1993). *Contexts that matter for teaching and learning.* Palo Alto, CA: Center for Research on the Context of Secondary School Teaching.

Meier, D. (1995). *The power of their ideas: Lessons for America from a small school in Harlem.* Boston, MA: Beacon Press.

Michigan Department of Education, & North Central Regional Educational Laboratory. (1998). *Connecting with the learner: An equity toolkit.* Retrieved January 24, 2002, from the North Central Regional Educational Laboratory Web site: http://www.ncrel.org/msc/products/connect.htm

Michigan Department of Education. (2001). *Professional development through learning communities: Ensuring cultures in Michigan schools in which all learners learn at high levels.* Lansing, MI: Author.

Mid-Atlantic Eisenhower Regional Consortium. (1997). *TIMSS eighth grade sourcebook.* Philadelphia, PA: Author.

References

Middleton, J. A., & Spanias, P. (1999). Motivation for achievement in mathematics: Findings, generalizations, and criticisms of the recent research. *Journal for Research in Mathematics Education, 30*(1), 65-88.

Mokros, J., Russell, S. J., & Economopoulos, K. (1995). *Beyond arithmetic: Changing mathematics in the elementary classroom.* Palo Alto, CA: Dale Seymour.

Moschkovich, J., & Schoenfeld, A. H. (1993). Aspects of understanding: On multiple perspectives and representation of linear relations and connections among them. In T. A. Romberg, E. Fennema, & T. P. Carpenter (Eds.), *Integrating research on the graphical representation of functions* (pp. 69-100). Hillsdale, NJ: Lawrence Erlbaum.

Moses, R. P., & Cobb, C. E., Jr. (2001). *Radical equations: Math literacy and civil rights.* Boston, MA: Beacon Press.

Moses, R., Kamii, C., Swap, S. M., & Howard, J. (1989, November). The algebra project: Organizing in the spirit of Ella. *Harvard Educational Review, 59*(4),423-443.

Muther, C. (1988). *Textbook adoption: A process for decision making. A workshop manual.* Manchester, CT: Textbook Adoption Advisory Services.

National Academy of Sciences. (1996). *Renewing U.S. mathematics.* Overhead package for *Curriculum and Evaluation Standards for School Mathematics 1989.* Reston, VA: National Council of Teachers of Mathematics

National Action Council for Minorities in Engineering (NACME). (2001, December). Math is power. Resource room. Retrieved January 24, 2002, from http://www.mathispower.org/intro1.html

National Center for Education Statistics (NCES). (1998, January). *Statistical analysis report. Parent involvement in children's education: Efforts by public elementary schools. NCES 98-032.* Retrieved January 24, 2002, from the NCES Web site: http://nces.ed.gov/pubs98/98032.html

National Center for Education Statistics. (2000). *Pursuing excellence: Comparison of 8th grade mathematics and science achievement from a U.S. perspective, 1985 and 1999.* Washington, DC: U. S. Government Printing Office.

National Commission on Excellence in Education. (1983). *A nation at risk: The imperative for educational reform.* Washington, DC: U.S. Government Printing Office.

National Commission on Mathematics and Science Teaching for the 21st Century. (2000). *Before it's too late: A report to the nation from the National Commission on Mathematics and Science Teaching for the 21st Century.* Washington, DC: U.S. Department of Education.

National Commission on Teaching and America's Future (1996). *What matters most: Teaching for America's future.* New York: Author.

National Council of Supervisors of Mathematics. (1997). *Supporting improvement in mathematics education: A public relations sourcebook,* pp. IIM4-IIM21. Golden, CO: Author.

National Council of Teachers of Mathematics. (1980). *An agenda for action: Recommendations for school mathematics of the 1980s.* Reston, VA: Author.

National Council of Teachers of Mathematics. (1989). *Curriculum and evaluation standards for school mathematics.* Reston, VA: Author.

National Council of Teachers of Mathematics. (1991). *Position statement on selecting instructional materials.* Reston, VA: Author.

National Council of Teachers of Mathematics. (1991). *Professional teaching standards for school mathematics.* Reston, VA: Author.

National Council of Teachers of Mathematics. (1995). *Assessment standards for school mathematics.* Reston, VA: Author.

National Council of Teachers of Mathematics. (1999). *Figure this! Math challenges for families, helping your child learn math.* Retrieved January 24, 2002, from www.figurethis.org/

National Council of Teachers of Mathematics. (2000). *Principles and standards for school mathematics.* Reston, VA: Author.

National Parent Teacher Association. (1997). *National PTA's national standards for parent/family involvement programs.* Retrieved January 24, 2002, from the National Parent Teacher Association Web site: http://www.pta.org/programs/invstand.htm

National Research Council. (1989). *Everybody counts: A report to the nation on the future of mathematics education.* Washington, DC: National Academy Press.

References

National Research Council. (1993). *Measuring what counts: A conceptual guide for mathematics assessment*. Washington, DC: National Academy Press.

National Research Council. (1999). *A guide for designing coherent curriculum programs in mathematics and science*. Washington, DC: National Academy Press.

National Research Council. (1999). *Designing mathematics or science curriculum programs: A guide for using mathematics and science education standards*. Washington, DC: National Academy Press.

National Research Council. (1999). *Global perspective for local action: Using TIMSS to improve U.S. mathematics and science education*. Washington, DC: National Academy Press.

National Research Council. (2000). *Inquiry and the national science education standards: A guide for teaching and learning*. Washington, DC: National Academy Press.

National Science Foundation. (1999). Inquiry thoughts, views, and strategies for the K–5 classroom. *(Foundations: A monograph for professionals in science, mathematics, and technology education, 2*, No. NSF 99-148). Arlington, VA: Author.

Newmann, F. M., & Wehlage, G. G. (1995). *Successful school restructuring: A report to the public and educators*. Madison, WI: Center on Organization and Restructuring of Schools.

Nunley, K. F. (1999). *The regular educator's guide to the brain*. Salt Lake City, UT: Nunley Associates.

O'Sullivan, C. Y., Reese, C. M., & Mazzeo, J. (1997). *NAEP 1996 science report card for the nation and states*. Washington, DC: National Center for Education Statistics.

Oakes, J. (1993). The tracking wars: Is anyone winning? *Harvard Education Letter, 8*(3), 1-4.

Payne, R. K. (1998). *A framework for understanding poverty*. (Rev. ed.). Baytown, TX: RFT Publishing.

Peressini, D., & Webb, N. (1999). *Analyzing mathematical reasoning in students' responses across multiple performance assessment tasks. In L. Stiff (Ed.), Developing mathematical reasoning in grades K–12*. Reston, VA: National Council of Teachers of Mathematics.

Perkins, D. (1993). Learning for understanding. *American Educator, 17*(3), 8, 28-35.

Porter, A. (1994). National standards and school improvement in the 1990s: Issues and promise. *American Journal of Education, 102*(4), 421-449.

Reese, C. M., Miller, K. E., Mazzeo, J., & Dossey, J. A. (1997). *NAEP 1996 mathematics report card for the nation and states*. Washington, DC: National Center for Education Statistics.

Resnick, L. B., & Klopfer, L. E. (1989). *Toward the thinking curriculum: Current cognitive research*. Alexandria, VA: Association for Supervision and Curriculum Development.

Resnick, L., Bill, V., Lesgold, S., & Leer, M. (1991). Thinking in arithmetic class. In B. Means, C. Chelemer, & M. Knapp (Eds.), *Teaching advanced skills to at-risk students: Views from research and practice* (pp. 27-53). San Francisco: Jossey-Bass.

Roempler, K. S. (1999). Using the Internet in the classroom: Becoming a critical consumer of the web. *ENC Focus, 6*(3), 11-13.

Romberg, T., & Kaput, J. (1999). Mathematics worth teaching, mathematics worth understanding. In E. Fenema & T. Romberg (Eds.), *Mathematics classrooms that promote understanding* (pp. 3-17). Mahwah, NJ: Lawrence Erlbaum.

Schiefele, U., & Csikszentmihalyi, M. (1995). Motivation and ability factors in mathematics experience and achievement. *Journal for Research in Mathematics Education, 226*(2), 163-181.

Schmidt, W., & Valverde, G. (1998). Refocusing U.S. math and science education. *Issues in Science and Technology, 14* (2), 60-66.

Secada, W. (1992). Race, ethnicity, social class, language and achievement in mathematics. In D. Grouws (Ed.), *Handbook of research on mathematics teaching and learning* (pp. 623-624). New York: Macmillan.

Shafer, M., & Romberg, T. A. (1999) Assessment in classrooms that promote understanding. In E. Fennema & T. A. Romberg (Eds.), *Mathematics classrooms that promote understanding* (pp. 159-184). Mahwah, NJ: Lawrence Erlbaum.

Shumway, R., White, A., Wheatley, G., Reys, R., Coburn, T., & Schoen, H. (1981, March). Initial effects of calculators in elementary school mathematics. *Journal for Research in Mathematics Education, 12*, 119-141.

References

Siegler, R. (1998). *Children's thinking*. Upper Saddle River, NJ: Prentice Hall.

Silver, H. F., Strong, R. W., & Perini, M. (2000). *So each may learn: Integrating learning styles and multiple intelligences*. Alexandria, VA: Association for Supervision and Curriculum Development.

Sizer, T. (1992). *Horace's school: Redesigning the American high school*. Boston, MA: Houghton Mifflin.

Sousa, D. A. (1995). *How the brain learns*. Reston, VA: National Association of Secondary School Principals.

Sowell, E. J. (1989). Effects of manipulative materials in mathematics instruction. *Journal for Research in Mathematics Education, 20*(5), 498-505.

Sparks, D. (1992). Merging content knowledge and pedagogy: An interview with Lee Shulman. *Journal of Staff Development, 13*(1), 14-17.

Sparks, D., & Hirsh, S. (1997). *A new vision for staff development*. Alexandria, VA: Association for Supervision and Curriculum Development.

Spoon, J., & Schell, J. (1998). Aligning student learning styles with instructor teaching styles. *Journal of Industrial Teacher Education, 35*(2). Retrieved January 24, 2002, from the Digital Library and Archives Web site: http://scholar.lib.vt.edu/ejournals/JITE/v35n2/spoon.html

Sprenger, M. (1999). *Learning and memory: The brain in action*. Alexandria, VA: Association for Supervision and Curriculum Development.

Steen, L. A. (1990). *On the shoulders of giants: New approaches to numeracy*. Washington, DC: National Academy Press.

Steffe, L. P., & Wiegel, H. G. (1996). On the nature of a model of mathematical learning. In L. P. Steffe, P. Nesher, P. Cobb, G. A. Goldin, & B. Greer (Eds.), *Theories of mathematical learning* (pp. 477-498). Mahwah, NJ: Lawrence Erlbaum.

Stenmark, J. K. (1989). *Assessment alternatives in mathematics: An overview of assessment techniques that promote learning*. Berkeley, CA: University of California Regents.

Stenmark, J. K. (Ed.). (1991). *Mathematics assessment: Myths, models, good questions, and practical suggestions*. Reston, VA: National Council of Teachers of Mathematics.

Stepanek, J., & Jarrett, D. (1997). *Assessment strategies to inform science and mathematics instruction. It's just good teaching series*. Portland, OR: Northwest Regional Educational Laboratory.

Stevenson, H. W., & Stigler, J. W. (1992). *The learning gap: Why our schools are failing and what we can learn from Japanese and Chinese education*. New York: Summit Books.

Stigler, J. W., & Hiebert, J. (1999). *The teaching gap: Best ideas from the world's teachers for improving education in the classroom*. New York: The Free Press.

Streefland, L. (1991). *Fractions in realistic mathematics education: A paradigm of developing research*. Dordrecht: Kluwer Academic Publishers.

Stroup, W. (1999, April). *The structure of generative activity in group settings*. Paper presented at the meeting of the American Educational Research Association, Montreal, Canada.

Suydam, M. N. (1985). Questions? Research report. *Arithmetic Teacher, 32*(6), 18.

Sylwester, R. (1995). *A celebration of neurons: An educator's guide to the human brain*. Alexandria, VA: Association for Supervision and Curriculum Development.

Texas Statewide Systemic Initiative, Charles A. Dana Center, University of Texas at Austin (1998). *Instructional materials analysis and selection for instructional materials implementation*. Retrieved January 23, 2002, from The Texas Education Network Web site: http://www.tenet.edu/teks/math/resources/instmaterialsas.html

The National Institute on Educational Governance, Finance, Policymaking, and Management, & Consortium for Policy Research in Education. (1998). *Policy brief: What the Third International Mathematics and Science Study (TIMSS) means for systemic school improvement*. Washington, DC: U.S. Department of Education, Office of Educational Research and Improvement.

Thompson, C., & Zeuli, J. (1999). The frame and the tapestry: Standards-based reform and professional development. In L. Darling-Hammond & G. Sykes, (Eds.), *Teaching as a learning profession: Handbook of policy and practice* (pp. 341-375). San Francisco, CA: Jossey-Bass.

Thorson, A. (Ed.). (2000). Mathematics and science in the real world. *ENC Focus, 7*(3).

References

Tobias, S. (1990). *They're not dumb, they're different: Stalking the second tier.* Tucson, AZ: Research Corporation.

Tomlinson, C. A. (1999). *The differentiated classroom: Responding to the needs of all learners.* Alexandria, VA: Association for Supervision and Curriculum Development.

Tsuruda, G. (1994). *Putting it together: Middle school math in transition.* Portsmouth, NH: Heinemann.

Tye, K. A. (1992). Restructuring our schools: Beyond the rhetoric. *Phi Delta Kappan, 74*(1), 8-14.

Tyson, H. (1997, July 30). *Overcoming structural barriers to good textbooks.* Retrieved January 24, 2002, from the National Education Goals Panel Web site: http://www.negp.gov/Reports/tyson.htm

U.S. Department of Education. (1997). *Attaining excellence: A TIMSS resource kit.* Washington, DC: U.S. Department of Education, Office of Educational Research and Improvement.

U.S. Department of Labor. (1993). *Learning a living: A blueprint for high performance (SCANS report).* Washington, DC: U.S. Government Printing.

Wellburn, E. (1996, May). *The status of technology in the education system: A literature review.* Retrieved January 24, 2002, from Community Learning Network Web site: http://www.cln.org/lists/nuggets/EdTech_report.html

Wenglinsky, H. (1998, September). *Does it compute? The relationship between educational technology and student achievement in mathematics.* Princeton, NJ: Educational Testing Service.

Wenglinsky, H. (2000). *How teaching matters: Bringing the classroom back into discussions of teacher quality.* Princeton, NJ: Milken Family Foundation.

Westwater, A., & Wolfe, P. (2000). The brain-compatible curriculum. *Educational Leadership, 58*(3), 49-52.

Wheatley, C. (1980). Calculator use and problem-solving performance. *Journal for Research in Mathematics Education, 11*, 323-333.

Willis, S. (2000). Portfolios: Helping students think about their thinking. *Education Update, 42*(4), 7.

Willoughby, S. S. (2000). Perspectives on mathematics education. In Burke, M. J., & Curcio, F. R. (Eds.). *Learning mathematics for a new century: 2000 yearbook* (pp. 1-15). Reston, VA: National Council of Teachers of Mathematics.

Wolfe, P. (2001). *Brain matters: Translating research into classroom practice.* Alexandria, VA: Association for Supervision and Curriculum Development.

Wu, H. (1999, Fall). Basic skills versus conceptual understanding: A bogus dichotomy in mathematics education. *American Educator*, 1-7.

Yackel, E., Cobb, P., Wood, T., Wheatley, G., & Merkel, G. (1990). The importance of social interaction in children's construction of mathematical knowledge. In *Teaching mathematics in the 1990s. 1990 yearbook* (pp. 12-21). Reston, VA: National Council of Teachers of Mathematics.

Yale Child Study Center, Comer School Development Program. (2001). *Program overview: The parent team.* Retrieved January 24, 2002, from Comer School Development Program Web site: http://info.med.yale.edu/comer/about/parent.html

Zemelman, S., Daniels, H., & Hyde, A. (1998). *Best practice: New standards for teaching and learning in America's schools.* Portsmouth, NH: Heinemann.

Index

Ability Grouping
  Differentiated instruction 4,5,9
  Homogeneous/ heterogeneous 4,5
  Impacts 4
  Teacher assignment 4,24

Accommodations for Students
  Disabilities, with 37,61,63
  Language learners 35,51
  Learning styles, with varied 8-9,91

Administrators 3,7,31,34,85

Algorithms 82-83

Assessment..33-41,52,53
  Alternative methods 34,35,36,37,53
  Consistent expectations 9
  Embedded 5,22,23,37,39,53
  Instruction, link with 22-23
  Mathematical thinking and reasoning, of 37,38-39
  National and international 40-41,48,74
  Learning styles, of 9
  Roles..23,34-35,36
  Rubrics 22,35,39,97
  Student self-..23,37
  Using data to improve instruction....................34,35,99

Attitudes, Student 18-19,22,29,86-87,90

Attitudes, Teacher 28-29,86,99

Basic Skills..80-81,97

Becoming a Nation of Readers 50

Before It's Too Late...74

Benchmarks for Science Literacy 54,96

Brain Research 73,76,92-93
  Learning styles 8

Calculators 62-63,64-65,80
  Graphing...62,64,65

Classroom Environment 3,6,7,18,19,78,84,87

Communication 8,14,19,25,39,51,69,94
  Discussion..44,77,88
  Questioning.........................15,16,17,21,24,37,76,77,79,96
  Reading and writing 37,50-51,88,89
  Reflecting...19,37,88-89,96

Constructivism 5,18,20,21,78,82,85,88

Counselors 2,6,7,41

Curriculum..43-59
  Coherence and articulation 5,41,45,48-49
  Connecting to outside world 7,13,25,39,44,46,
                                                      54,58-59,62,68,92,96
  Culturally responsive..6,7
  Integrated mathematics approach 56-57,70,92,99
  Integrated with other disciplines 53,54-55,92
  Principle..44
  Reading and writing in mathematics 50-51
  Standards-based..................................7,44-45,46-47,49,53

Curriculum and Evaluation Standards for
  School Mathematics 46,59

Equity 1-9
  Ethnicity 2,8,40,86
  Evidence in classrooms 2-3,6
  Gender 2,40,61,64,86
  Principle...1
  SES (socioeconomic status) 2,40,87

Glenn Commission Report (See Before It's Too Late.)

Homework...96-97

Inquiry Approach to Problem Solving 21,62,65

Instructional Materials Selection 45,52-53

Instructional Strategies/Methods 3,13,15,21,
                                      25,41,62,66,70,71,90-91,92-93
  Differentiated 4,5,9
  Diverse student populations, for 5,6,7
  Inquiry 14,47,65
  Learner-centered 5,6,8,9,20-21,
                                                      66-67,78-79

Instructional Technology 19,53,61-71
  Authentic use...66,68,70
  Benefits of using.................................7,25,61,64,65,66
  Changes in importance of topics 70-71,80,82
  Learner-centered instruction using 66-67
  Mathematics reasoning, uses in 62-63
  Problem solving, uses in 62-63,64,70

International Comparisons 22,40-41,44,48,64,86

Index

Internet Data
    Comparison to textbooks 68
    Credibility of..69
    Instructional uses 68-69

Learning...73-99
    Active hands-on 13,15,67,84,90-91,
        92-93,96
    Contextual 5,7,18,25,46,76,77,
        85,92-93,94-95
    Principle 78
    Style..8-9,78
    Style mismatch 9
    Teacher learning, impact on student 98-99
    Theory..78-79

Manipulatives (See also Instructional
    Technology.) 13,19,53,76,77,
        90-91,92-93

Mathematics
    Algebra 2,7,46,48,56,62,74,
        77,80,81
    Algorithms 82-83
    Basic skills..80-81,97
    Computation 80-81,82
    Connections 14,15,56,77
    Experts 96
    Gatekeeper, as 2,6,46
    Geometry 2,7,46,48,56,62,67,74,80
    Habits of mind 46,96
    Integrated 56-57,92
    Literacy 1,4,46,74,75,80
    Number sense 47,82
    Principles and standards 74,75
    Problem solving......................12-13,14,47,76,84
    Reasoning 12-13,14,15,38,
        47,53,84
    Representations 14,15,25,47,56,62,81,91
    Value (relevance)...74-75

Mathematics Education
    Assessment..33-41
    Curriculum 43-59
    For all 1-9
    Instructional technology.............................61-71
    Learning 73-99
    Teaching 11-31

Metacognition 8,19,20,23,88-89,92

Misconceptions, Student...........................17,20,23,79,85,99

Motivation, Student 18-19,51,54,68,69,78

National Assessment of Educational
    Progress (NAEP)..40

National Council of Teachers of
    Mathematics (NCTM)................................51,74

NCTM *Standards* (See *PSSM*.)

Opportunity to Learn (OTL)....................................4,6-7,76

Parent Involvement and Support 3,34,41,75,94-95

Parent Teacher Organization (PTA, PTO) 94-95

Principles and Standards for School Mathematics (See *PSSM*.)

Professional Development 3,7,22,25,27,29,
        37,41,52,84,98-99
    Design...30-31,41
    Strategies..31,45
    Technology, about 63,71

PSSM 1,11,15,26,33,43,
        44,46,48,61,73,74,78,85,87,98

Staff Development (See Professional Development.)

Standards (See *PSSM*.)

Success Factors in Student Learning 18,84-85,88

Teacher
    Attitudes, beliefs, expectations 19,22,28-29,86
    Content knowledge..........................3,6,18,24-25,84,98,99
    Learning affects student learning 98-99
    Pedagogical knowledge 3,17,20,25,26-27,84
    Quality 18,27,37,84,85,87,98

    Teaching 11-31
    Principle 98
    Styles 8-9

Technology (See also Instructional Technology.)
    Principle 63,68

Textbook Selection (See Instructional Materials Selection.)

TIMSS (Third International Mathematics and Science
    Study)..40,48,74

Tracking (See Ability Grouping.)

Value of Learning Mathematics 74-75